NEW Close-up A2

Phillip McElmuray

NATIONAL GEOGRAPHIC
LEARNING

Australia • Brazil • Canada • Mexico • Singapore • United Kingdom • United States

CREDITS

Reading reading for main ideas; multiple choice with one text

1 Read the Exam Reminder. What can you do with the key words in each paragraph of a text?

Exam REMINDER

Reading for main ideas
- Find the most important information first. It helps you understand the text.
- What's the main idea of each paragraph?
- Look at each paragraph. What are the key words about the main idea? Underline them.

2 Now read the text and complete the Exam Task.

Exam TASK

Multiple choice with one text

For each question, choose the correct answer.

1 What country do the von Engelbrechtens live in?
  A Tonga
  B New Zealand
  C Australia

2 What nationality is Karyn?
  A German
  B British
  C Tongan

3 Why is their house on a hill?
  A to have a good view
  B to keep it safe from the sea
  C to be close to drinking water

4 The family get their food
  A from only their island.
  B from a smaller island.
  C from their island and another island.

5 Jack goes to school in New Zealand
  A to get a better education.
  B to spend time with other students.
  C to be around nature.

Alone on an island

Fofoa island

The von Engelbrechten family live in a very unusual place. Their home is on the small island of Fofoa and they are the only people who live there. Fofoa is about one kilometre long and the island is part of Tonga, a country in the South Pacific Ocean. It is quite close to other islands in Tonga, but it is about 1,800 kilometres from New Zealand and around 4,000 kilometres from Australia.

There are five people in the von Engelbrechten family – Karyn, the mother, who is from the UK; Boris, the father, who is from Germany; and their three sons Jack, Luca and Felix. They've got a two-bedroom home on a small hill with an amazing view of the ocean. The house is high up because they don't want the ocean to come into their living room!

The family drink rainwater and grow fruit and vegetables on the island. Sometimes, they travel to a larger island nearby to bring back food.

Karyn and Boris are happy to have nature around them, and Luca and Felix enjoy their life on the island. Jack, the oldest son, lives in New Zealand now. He goes to school there because he wants to be around other young people. Karyn teaches Luca and Felix on the island. She makes sure that they get a good education, just like children who go to school.

Vocabulary 1 countries and nationalities; numbers and dates

1 Complete the sentences with the correct country or nationality.

1 Jake is from England. He's _____ .

2 Emi is Japanese. She's from _____ .

3 Henry speaks Vietnamese because he lives in _____ .

4 Mario loves Italian lasagne. This food is from _____ .

5 José lives in Bolivia, but he's from Spain. He's _____ .

6 Michele lives in Paris, France. This city is the _____ capital.

7 Eleni lives on an island in Greece. It's a _____ island.

8 Francisca lives in Brazil. She really loves _____ beaches.

9 Kofi is from Ghana, but his wife is from the US. His wife is _____ .

10 Carla is Portuguese because she's from Madeira and Madeira is part of _____ .

2 Write the correct countries next to the nationalities.

1 Australian _____

2 Egyptian _____

3 Polish _____

4 Bolivian _____

5 Kazakhstani _____

6 Malaysian _____

7 Ghanaian _____

8 Greenlandic _____

3 Write the numbers in words.

1 4 _____

2 18 _____

3 22 _____

4 39 _____

5 41 _____

6 57 _____

7 60 _____

8 73 _____

9 85 _____

10 96 _____

4 The dates in the diary are in British English. Write the date as we say it.

My diary

Birthdays

Jake	07/04	the seventh of April
Emi	03/08	_____
Henry	19/02	_____
Mario	24/01	_____
José	02/05	_____
Michel	31/07	_____
Eleni	05/03	_____
Francisca	12/09	_____

5 Now write the birthdays from Exercise 4 as we write them.

1 Jake _____

2 Emi _____

3 Henry _____

4 Mario _____

5 José _____

6 Michel _____

7 Eleni _____

8 Francisca _____

6 Write the months that are NOT in Exercise 4.

1 _____

2 _____

3 _____

4 _____

7 Complete the sentences with your own information.

All about me!

1 My name's _____ .

2 I'm from _____ .

3 I'm _____ years old.

4 My birthday is on _____ .

5 My favourite day of the year is _____ .

Grammar 1 present simple; adverbs of frequency; question words

1 Read the paragraph and underline the verbs in the present simple form.

My name is Li Chen. I live in China. I'm 12 years old and I go to school in Beijing.

I've got two close friends, Chyou and Meilin, and we have lunch together at school. Meilin's got a really cool bike. She rides it to school every day. Chyou and I haven't got bikes, so we walk to school or take the bus.

At weekends, we meet in the park or we play computer games at my house. On Saturdays, we sometimes go to the cinema. I enjoy our time together a lot!

2 Complete the sentences with the present simple form of the verbs.

1 _____ (you / study) every day after school?

2 _____ (Chen / play) the piano?

3 I _____ (not like) cola.

4 Maria _____ (not / have) a smartphone.

5 Louis _____ (never / talk) during class.

6 My brothers _____ (always / be) late for dinner.

7 We _____ (hardly ever / travel) abroad for holidays.

8 Yusef _____ (often / be) helpful around the house.

9 Jayden _____ (not / walk) to school.

10 They _____ (never / go) to the library.

3 Complete the questions with these words.

what	what time	when	where
who	why		

1 **A:** _____ is your favourite book?

B: *Charlotte's Web.*

2 **A:** _____ is Murat?

B: He's in the library.

3 **A:** _____ is the new student?

B: His name is Alexis.

4 **A:** _____ do you usually study?

B: After school or at the weekend.

5 **A:** Fabio, _____ do you have photography lessons?

B: Because I really like taking photos.

6 **A:** _____ does your music lesson start?

B: 6.30 p.m.

Listening listening to instructions; gap fill

1 Read the Exam Reminder. What do we sometimes find out about the conversation from the instructions?

_____

2 **1.1 ▶** **Listen and complete the Exam Task.**

Exam **TASK**

Gap fill

For each question, write the correct answer in the gap. Write **one word** or a **number** or a **date** or a **time**.

You will hear a teacher telling her students about a reading club at a library.

Summer clubs

Place: Wellington Library

Club: Reading

Number of times per week:
(1) _____

Total number of weeks:
(2) _____ weeks

Dates of club: 20th July to 31st
(3) _____

Start time of club: **(4)** _____ a.m.

Cost to join club: **(5)** £ _____

↻ Grammar References 1.1, 1.2 and 1.3, p161 in Student's Book

Vocabulary 2 family

1 Choose the correct words to complete the text.

My family

My name's Miguel. I'm thirteen years old and I live in Guatemala. I love football – I play for the boys' team at school. I've got a ¹ *brother / sister*, Maria, and she is eleven years old. I've also got a ² *sister / brother*, Diego, and he's nine. Maria, Diego and I live with our ³ *cousins / parents* in a house in the countryside. My ⁴ *father / mother*, Luis, is 43 and he is a teacher. My ⁵ *father / mother*, Lucinda, is 38 and she's a scientist. My ⁶ *grandparents / parents* also live with us, which is great because Maria, Diego and I get on really well with them. Frida is my ⁷ *grandmother / grandfather* and she's 68. Pedro is my ⁸ *grandmother / grandfather* and it's his seventieth birthday party today. My father's brother is here for the party — that's my ⁹ *aunt / uncle* Juan. He's with his son, my ¹⁰ *nephew / cousin* Enrico. My mother's sister, my ¹¹ *aunt / uncle* Yolanda, is here as well. We like big family parties!

2 What other words can we use for family members? Complete the sentences with these words.

| dad daddy grandma granny |
| grandad grandpa mum mummy |

1 Luis is Miguel's _____ or _____ .

2 Lucinda is Miguel's _____ or _____ .

3 Frida is Miguel's _____ or _____ .

4 Pedro is Miguel's _____ or _____ .

3 Complete the table with these words.

| aunt brother cousin daughter father |
| grandad granny husband mother |
| nephew niece sister son uncle wife |

Men / Boys	Women / Girls	Both

4 The words in bold are wrong. Write the correct word. Use the text in Exercise 1 to help you.

1 Miguel is Luis's **daughter**. _____

2 Maria is Lucinda's **niece**. _____

3 Luis is Lucinda's **son**. _____

4 Lucinda is Luis's **nephew**. _____

5 Miguel is Juan's **husband**. _____

6 Maria is Yolanda's **wife**. _____

5 Complete the sentences with the correct words.

1 Miguel is Maria's _____ , Lucinda's _____ , Yolanda's _____ and Enrico's _____ .

2 Maria is Diego's _____ , Luis's _____ , Juan's _____ and Enrico's _____ .

3 Lucinda is Maria's _____ , Enrico's _____ and Yolanda's _____ .

4 Luis is Diego's _____ , Juan's _____ and Enrico's _____ .

5 Frida is Pedro's _____ and Maria's _____ .

6 Enrico is Miguel's _____ , Juan's _____ and Lucinda's _____ .

7 Yolanda is Lucinda's _____ and Diego's _____ .

8 Pedro is Frida's _____ and Miguel's _____ .

Grammar 2 present continuous; writing the missing words; open cloze

1 Underline the verbs in the present continuous form.

1 Mauricio is a musician. He's playing the guitar right now.

2 Francesca and Ana like the Korean language. They're learning the alphabet at the moment.

3 Eduardo's riding his bike to school. His lessons start at 8.20 a.m.

4 Yolanda's running for the bus. It's leaving.

5 I'm looking for some new shoes. My other shoes are really old.

6 Why are we waiting here? I want to go.

7 We're doing our maths homework. It's for Mrs Ravachol.

8 Julietta isn't in my violin class. She isn't practising the violin at the moment.

2 Complete the sentences with the present continuous form of the verbs.

1 Tomas _____ (buy) a new pair of trousers for school.

2 I _____ (write) an email to my friend Annika in South Africa.

3 Dana and Sam _____ (not / chat) online. They _____ (play) computer games.

4 Mum's ill. _____ (Dad / make) dinner tonight?

5 There are a lot of people here for the school play. Where _____ (your parents / sit)?

6 Why _____ (Yuri / wait) for Erika? She's not at school today.

7 Hijumi _____ (spend) the weekend with her cousin.

8 Tadeo _____ (not do) his homework. He _____ (watch) TV.

3 Complete the sentences with the present continuous form of these verbs.

get	have	listen	not answer
not watch	study		

1 I _____ a film.

2 Kim _____ for his exam.

3 We _____ ready for the party.

4 _____ (you) to me?

5 They usually go home for lunch, but they _____ lunch at school this week.

6 Ahmed _____ his phone.

4 Read the Exam Reminder and complete the Exam Task.

Exam REMINDER

Writing the missing words
- First, read the whole text to understand the main idea.
- Think about what type of word goes in each gap.
- Read the text again. Fill in the gaps, then check your answers. Do they make sense?
- Read the text again. Is your spelling correct?

Exam TASK

Open cloze

For each question, write the correct answer.

Write **one** word for each gap.

Email Message
From: Natalie
To: Hala

Hi Hala

How are you? How is your cousin from Jordan? Are you **(1)** _____ a good time with him? **(2)** _____ are you doing together today? We also have a guest: my cousin Veronica **(3)** _____ staying with us for the weekend. I usually go **(4)** _____ her flat on Saturdays, but her parents **(5)** _____ working this weekend, so we're here. We're making a banana cake. I love it – it's **(6)** _____ favourite!

Love

Natalie

Grammar Reference 1.4, p161 in Student's Book

Writing focusing on accuracy; completing a form

Learning **REMINDER**

Focusing on accuracy

You often give this information when you complete a form: your title, your first name and surname, your date of birth or age, where you were born, where you live, your phone number and your email address.

1 Write the sections of a form next to the correct information.

> Date of birth   Email address   Home address
> Interests   Name   Title

1 _____ : Ms
2 _____ : Peggy Simpson
3 _____ : 15th May 2001
4 _____ : 24 Amwell Street, Brighton, UK
5 _____ : psimpson@mail.com
6 _____ : reading books, listening to music

2 Read the task. Then decide if the statements (1–4) are true (T) or false (F).

> You want to join a volunteer clean-up programme. Complete the form.
>
> On the form:
> - use a pen to write information about yourself (e.g. your name and address)
> - ask when the clean-up is happening next
> - ask if you need to bring anything with you on the day

1 The form asks for your name and address. ☐
2 You can complete the form in pencil. ☐
3 The form tells you the date when the programme starts. ☐
4 On the form there's a list of things you need to have with you when you begin. ☐

3 Read the example form and correct the eight mistakes.

4 Complete the form with your own information. Don't forget to use the Useful Language on page 15 of your Student's Book.

Help older people and their pets

We are looking for kind volunteers to help older people look after their pets.

- buy pet food
- take dogs for walks and play with other animals
- spend time with the owners and their pets

Complete the application form with your details and tell us why you want to help people and their pets.

> **Application Form**
>
> Title: _____
> First name: _____
> Surname: _____
> DOB: ____ /____ /____
> Nationality: _____
> Address: _____
> _____
> Email: _____
> Phone number: _____
> Explain why you want to join our project:
> _____
> _____
> _____
> _____
> _____
> Questions:
> _____
> _____
> _____

Beach **Watch Programme**

Check the title is correct.

Title (please tick)
► Miss ✔ Mr ☐ Ms ☐ Mrs ☐

Check the first name and surname are in the correct gaps.

First name
► Hendricks

Surname
Sam

Check the date format.

Date of Birth
► 2000, 7th May

Street address
18 Montpelier Road

City, Postcode, Country
CF10 1AC, UK, Cardiff

Check the parts of the address are in the correct order.

Explain why you want to help with our programme:
I like visit the beach, but I don't like seeing rubbish on the beaches. I really want to help tidy it up.

Questions
When the next clean-up?
Do I need to bring anything with me?

Reading finding specific information; multiple matching

1 Read the Exam Reminder. What can you do if you can't find the key words from the questions in the texts?

_____

2 Now read the texts and complete the Exam Task.

Exam **TASK**

Multiple matching

For each question, choose the correct answer.

		Fidelia	Logan	Thahn
1	Who talks about something people wore in the past?	A	B	C
2	Who talks about giving things to other people?	A	B	C
3	Who describes a type of competition?	A	B	C
4	Who played music during the festival?	A	B	C
5	Who made something to wear?	A	B	C
6	Whose festival happens twice on the same day of the week?	A	B	C
7	Who talks about using something from nature?	A	B	C

My world, my clothes

Fidelia Every summer in the city of Oaxaca, Mexico, we have the Guelaguetza festival. We wear bright clothes with red, orange, yellow and green – the colours of fruit. We have the festival on the last two Mondays of July. I was in the festival this year. My sister and I did a traditional dance with other women in the city. We held fruit above our heads while we danced to music. The festival is about food and sharing, so we share meals and gifts.

Logan I come from a town called Dunoon in Scotland and, every year, we have the Cowal Highland Gathering. We wear 'kilts' – a type of skirt. Scottish men first wore them in the 1700s. In last year's festival, my dad, my brother and I all wore kilts. We walked through the town and we played traditional Scottish instruments. There is also a sports event. Players in kilts throw a big piece of wood up into the air. There are prizes for the winners. It's really fun to watch.

Vocabulary 1 clothes and colours

1 **Complete the sentences with words for clothing and accessories.**

1 Hélène, don't leave the house without your
  j _ _ _ _ _ . It's cold today.

2 We're going to the beach. I'm wearing a white
  T-shirt and my new pair of blue **s** _ _ _ _ _ .

3 These **s** _ _ _ _ _ _ are not good for my feet.
  I don't like walking in them.

4 You can put many things in this **h** _ _ _ _ _ _ ,
  such as your mobile phone, pens and paper.

5 Frank is wearing a black **s** _ _ _ and a tie for his
  first day of work.

6 Those **t** _ _ _ _ _ _ _ look great on you, but
  they are a bit too long.

7 That gold **n** _ _ _ _ _ _ _ is lovely. It looks like it
  cost a lot of money.

8 It's sunny today, so I will wear a big **h** _ _ to keep
  the sun off my face.

9 I wear **t** _ _ _ _ _ _ _ for basketball practice
  because I run a lot.

10 I'm ready for the party. I'm wearing a beautiful,
  long **d** _ _ _ _ .

2 **Look at the photo on page 23 of the Student's Book. Complete the sentences about the photo with these words.**

black	pink	red	silver	stripy	white

1 The first man on the left is wearing a _____
  shirt.

2 The first woman on the left is wearing a
  _____ shirt and a _____ necklace.

3 The second man on the left is wearing a
  _____ shirt and a _____ cap.

4 The last woman on the right is wearing a
  _____ , white and blue shirt.

3 **Read the sentences and choose the word that does not fit.**

1 I'm a bit cold. Can I borrow your *jumper* /
  handbag / *jacket*?

2 At the ceremony the President wore *a suit* /
  a shirt / *trainers*.

3 She's going for a run and she needs her *skirt* /
  socks / *trainers*.

4 The sun is very strong today. Have you got a *belt* /
  hat / *cap* to cover your head?

5 We're going for a walk in the forest and we need
  good *boots* / *trainers* / *sandals*.

6 Is that what you're planning to wear to your sister's
  wedding? I think you also need some accessories,
  like a nice *dress* / *hat* / *necklace*.

7 In summer, I usually wear *sandals* / *shorts* /
  a jumper.

4 **Complete the sentences with your own ideas.**

1 For school, I wear _____
  _____ .

2 When I do sports, I wear _____
  _____ .

3 On special days, I wear _____
  _____ .

4 My favourite clothes are _____
  _____ .

5 Today, I'm wearing _____
  _____ .

6 I don't like wearing _____
  _____ .

Thahn I live in Huê, Vietnam. Huê has got a
lot of history and, every two years, we have the
Huê Traditional Craft Festival for art, clothing and
medicine. There is a very interesting type of hat at the
festival – the *non la*, which is part of the traditional
Vietnamese costume. We use two different plants to
make the hats for the festival.

The hat looks very easy to make, but it takes all day to
make one. I tried it and it was quite difficult! I wore my
non la hat at the festival because it was a warm, sunny day.

Grammar 1 past simple; used to

1 Complete the sentences with the past simple form of the verbs.

1 Mila and Savannah _____ (wear) new uniforms on the first day of school.

2 Yasemin _____ (think) about wearing purple socks to school.

3 We _____ (go) to the beach after class.

4 I can't believe you _____ (eat) the whole burger!

5 There's some water in the bottle. I _____ (not drink) it all!

6 I _____ (not buy) an expensive present for my friend Awa's birthday.

7 Our teacher, Mr Joseph, _____ (show) us a film about festivals in Trinidad.

8 Tassos _____ (study) French at university.

2 Rewrite the sentences as yes / no questions.

1 You wore your red dress to the party.

_____

2 They brought enough food for the festival.

_____

3 They bought socks at the shopping centre.

_____

4 He was at the parade all day.

_____

5 You finished your homework on time.

_____

3 Complete the sentences with the correct form of used to and the verbs.

1 My mum _____ (wear) jeans all the time, but now she doesn't.

2 I ride a bike to school now, but I _____ (take) the bus.

3 They _____ (not have) such awful clothes in this shop.

4 Mum, _____ (you / play) in a band when you were a teenager?

5 I _____ (like) bright, colourful clothes, but now I prefer dark colours.

6 Gilberto, _____ (you and your family / go) to the carnival in Rio de Janeiro when you lived there?

Listening identifying the correct answer; multiple choice with five conversations

1 Read the Exam Reminder. How many conversations will you hear?

_____

2 [2.1] ▶ Listen and complete the Exam Task.

Exam TASK

Multiple choice with five conversations

For each question, choose the correct answer.

1 You will hear a girl talking to a friend about her new dress. What is she unhappy about?
   A the colour
   B the way it looks
   C the belt

2 You will hear a boy talking to his dad about his trainers. What is the problem?
   A The boy lost his trainers after football practice.
   B The trainers are too small.
   C They are very old.

3 You will hear a girl talking to her mum about an accident. How did she get home?
   A She walked home.
   B A family friend brought her home.
   C Her mum brought her home.

4 You will hear a girl talking to her brother. What does she want to borrow?
   A a jumper
   B a jacket
   C a hat

5 You will hear a woman talking about a present from her friend, Sophie. What did Sophie give her?
   A a summer dress
   B a handbag
   C a pair of shoes

▶ **Grammar References 2.1, p161; 2.2, p162 in Student's Book**

Vocabulary 2 adjectives to describe people

1 Match the adjectives (1–10) with the definitions (a–j).

1 brave ☐
2 busy ☐
3 careful ☐
4 clever ☐
5 friendly ☐
6 funny ☐
7 kind ☐
8 noisy ☐
9 quiet ☐
10 tired ☐

a loves talking to people
b needs to sleep or rest
c pays attention to what he or she is doing
d understands and learns quickly
e doesn't talk much
f always has a lot to do
g always helps other people
h makes other people laugh a lot
i talks loudly
j isn't easily scared

2 Choose the correct words to complete the sentences.

1 Carolina gets good marks at school because she's *clever / busy*.
2 Mert doesn't talk much. He's a rather *quiet / kind* person.
3 Billal is really *funny / happy*. He knows some great jokes and he always makes me laugh.
4 My mum is a police officer and her job is sometimes dangerous. I think she's really *quiet / brave*.
5 Selena, your notes are very *boring / useful*. I can understand the lesson much better now!
6 Please be *useful / careful* when you take this exam. The questions are not easy.

3 Complete the sentences with the correct adjectives. Use -ed or -ing and the verb in brackets.

1 I often get _____ (bore) when I go shopping. I only go when I need to buy something.
2 That film was very _____ (interest). I loved the ending!
3 Some classes are _____ (bore), but it's still good for you to learn about the subject.
4 Shelley was really _____ (tire), so she slept all afternoon.
5 Jean-Luc wasn't _____ (interest) in the show, so he left early.
6 I think exercise is very _____ (tire), but it's good for our health.

4 Complete the sentences with the correct form of these words.

beauty	care	friend	love	noise

1 My dog looks angry, but she's actually quite _____ .
2 That's a _____ dress. Where did you buy it?
3 My dad is very _____ in his work. He wants to do everything right.
4 It's quite _____ in here, Naomi. I can't hear you.
5 My grandmother is _____ and I really like spending time with her.

5 Complete the sentences with these words.

beautiful	brave	busy	clever	friendly
funny	happy	noisy		

1 My mum is always very _____ and she often works until late.
2 The children are very _____ today. Tell them to be quiet.
3 Amy's very _____ and she always makes her little brother laugh.
4 I'm glad everybody in my new school is very _____ – I've got lots of new friends.
5 Granny says that when she was young, you needed to be very _____ to go to the dentist.
6 That's a _____ picture. You're good at drawing.
7 Ahmed likes people and he's always _____ in large groups.
8 I don't know how to do this, but ask Jane. She's very _____ and I'm sure she knows.

6 Write all the adjectives you know that mean the opposite.

1 scared _____
2 bored _____
3 funny _____
4 sad _____
5 noisy _____
6 boring _____

Grammar 2 past continuous

1 Complete the sentences with the past simple or past continuous form of the verbs.

1 I _____ (send) an email when you _____ (call).

2 It was a beautiful morning. The birds _____ (sing) and the sun _____ (shine).

3 The lights _____ (go) out when Thea _____ (swim) in the indoor pool.

4 Hijumi _____ (talk), but we _____ (not listen).

5 Ammar _____ (run) to catch the bus when he _____ (fall) over.

6 Mr Lopez was having a bad day at school. The children _____ (talk) a lot in class and the classroom equipment _____ (not work) properly.

2 Choose the correct answers.

Lucia: How was the festival, Mateo?

Mateo: It was brilliant. I really ¹ _____ it.

Lucia: That's good to hear. Tell me more about it. What ² _____ ?

Mateo: Well, there was a really cool parade. I ³ _____ on the side of the street all day and I ⁴ _____ the people in the festival. They ⁵ _____ blue and white costumes.

Lucia: That sounds good. What ⁶ _____ in the parade?

Mateo: They ⁷ _____ while other people behind them ⁸ _____ music.

Lucia: Well, I'm glad you had a good time! Was the festival on Leandro Street?

Mateo: No, it ⁹ _____ there. They ¹⁰ _____ it on Leandro Street, but it's on Florida Street now.

Lucia: Oh, I see. I ¹¹ _____ to piano lessons on Florida Street, but I don't anymore.

1	**A** was enjoying	**B** enjoyed	**C** used to enjoy
2	**A** did you use to do	**B** were you doing	**C** did you do
3	**A** was standing	**B** were standing	**C** used to stand
4	**A** were watching	**B** used to watch	**C** was watching
5	**A** used to wear	**B** were wearing	**C** was wearing
6	**A** were doing	**B** they were doing	**C** were they doing
7	**A** were dancing	**B** was dancing	**C** used to dance
8	**A** wasn't playing	**B** were playing	**C** was playing
9	**A** wasn't	**B** weren't having	**C** wasn't having
10	**A** had	**B** were having	**C** used to have
11	**A** was going	**B** used to go	**C** didn't go

3 Think about a festival or a special day. Write five sentences about what happened and what the people were doing / wearing.

Name of festival / special day: _____

1 _____ .

2 _____ .

3 _____ .

4 _____ .

5 _____ .

▶ Grammar Reference 2.3, p162 in Student's Book

Writing writing about personality; including all the points; writing an email

Learning REMINDER
Writing about personality
- You can talk about good qualities and bad qualities to describe a person's personality.
- Use examples in your descriptions.
- Use these phrases and linking words: *so, and, because, but, that's why, for example*

1 Complete the sentences with these linking words and phrases.

and	because	but	for example
so	that's why		

1 Ayman is a good student. _____ , he studies every night and he also helps other students.
2 Maguette is a bit shy, _____ she doesn't go out much.
3 Daniella isn't a good friend _____ she said horrible things about me to Rosa.
4 I usually wear colourful clothes, _____ today I decided to wear black.
5 Michelle spends a lot of time playing basketball, and _____ she's a really good player.
6 I spend time with Oscar at the weekends _____ we chat online during the week.

2 Read the Exam Reminder. Which number do you need to check?

Exam REMINDER
Including all the points
- Check how many points you need to include. There are usually three points. You must include all of them in your answer.
- Underline the key words in the writing task to check you understand each point.
- Plan your email and write a draft before you write your final answer.

3 Read the writing task and answer the questions.
1 What do you need to write? _____
2 How many points do you need to include?
_____

You started a new school a month ago. Write an email to your friend about your new school.

In your email:
- talk about your new friend Tomas
- say where you met Tomas
- talk about the things that you and Tomas do together.

Write **25 words** or more.

4 Read a student's answer to the writing task. Choose the correct linking words.

Hi Pavlos

Tomas is really nice, [1] *so / because* I'm happy we moved here now. He's very funny; [2] *because / that's why* I like him so much. He makes everyone laugh [3] *so / and* he's very kind. We met at school in a maths class, [4] *but / that's why* we didn't speak to each other until lunch break. We often go to the park together [5] *for example / because* we both like playing football.

Write soon!

Joseph

5 Read the answer again. Has the writer included all the points in the writing task?

6 Read and complete the Exam Task. Don't forget to use the Useful Language on page 27 of your Student's Book.

Exam TASK
Writing an email
You want to tell your friend Amira about your first day of school. Write an email to Amira.

In your email:
- talk about your new English teacher
- say what you talked about in class with the other students
- ask how your friend's first day of school was.

Write **25 words** or more.

Reading thinking about context; multiple choice with six texts

1 Read the Exam Reminder. What is the context of a text?

a a type of reading exam

b where and when you may see the text

c a clue

2 Now read the texts and complete the Exam Task.

Exam TASK

Multiple choice with six texts

For each question, choose the correct answer.

1

> **FOR SALE:** laptop, printer, tablet. £250 for all.
>
> Tablet and laptop are one year old. Printer is two years old, needs a new part.
>
> **Call Boris on 7989302815**

A Boris is selling these things because they're old.

B All of the things need to be fixed.

C Boris is selling everything for one price.

2

> Hey Khalish,
> I just saw your message. Sorry for the late reply. I've got a problem with my laptop and I can't meet you today. How about tomorrow? Let me know if that's OK.
> Aqil.

A Aqil wants help with a laptop.

B Aqil is changing a meeting time.

C Aqil is late for the meeting.

3

> From: Katerina
> To: Melina
>
> Are you still free this evening? Remember to bring your digital camera with you. We can download the photos from the school trip onto my computer and print them on my new printer. See you soon!

A Katerina has got a new digital camera.

B Katerina wants to print some photos.

C Katerina is going on a school trip.

4

> The Stanford Science Museum is looking for a friendly person to work at the museum café. Must be 18 years or older. Hours are Monday to Friday from 10 a.m. to 4 p.m. Please go to the café to complete a form.

A You must go to the museum if you are interested in the job.

B You need to work weekends for this job.

C You must be a friendly teenager for this job.

5

> **Want to improve your computer skills?**
>
> Tech Centre is offering courses for beginners for £19 a week. Courses are in the evening, so you don't need to miss school or work!
>
> Call us on 7944654321 for more information.

A Courses are for people with excellent computer skills.

B People can take the courses late in the day.

C You need to call the number for course prices.

6

> From: Michelle Wu
> To: Mr Booth
>
> Your mobile phone is ready. We fixed the problem with the screen this morning. The service is free because you bought the phone a few days ago. We are very sorry for the problem.
>
> Best wishes,
> Michelle Wu
> Customer Service Representative

A The company is offering Mr Booth a free phone.

B Mr Booth doesn't need to pay.

C Mr Booth's phone still isn't working.

Vocabulary 1 technology; compound nouns; multiple-choice cloze

1 Choose the correct words to complete the sentences.

1 My eyes hurt from looking at a *screen / printer* all day.

2 Can I use your *digital camera / mobile phone* to make a call?

3 You need to put paper in the *laptop / printer* before you can use it.

4 I can't check my email because I forgot my *password / file*.

5 I do my work on *internet / a tablet* so I can work anywhere I like.

6 I prefer *laptops / screens* to ordinary computers because they're smaller.

7 I've got a lot of big video *screens / files* on my computer.

8 Can you *send / call* me tomorrow morning?

9 I always go *online / the web* at weekends.

10 I *entered / downloaded* the film last night. We can watch it together.

2 Complete the sentences with these words.

change	chat	check	download
send	text		

1 How often do you _____ with friends online?

2 I need to _____ my password. It's too easy to guess.

3 I _____ a lot of messages to my friends at the weekends.

4 It takes a long time to _____ big files.

5 Can you _____ me when you get home?

6 I _____ my email every morning after breakfast.

3 Complete the sentences with the correct words for technology or compound nouns.

1 I taught my granny how to _____ a file from the internet.

2 Lisa still sends _____ , but I prefer messaging.

3 Which _____ media are you on?

4 I used to use my mobile phone to take photos, but now I have a great _____ , and the photos are much better.

5 The yellow light means that your _____ has almost no ink.

4 Read the Exam Reminder and complete the Exam Task.

Exam **REMINDER**

Compound nouns

- We make a compound noun when we put two nouns together.
- Sometimes one word from a compound noun completes the gap in a text. For example, *computer* games.
- Check the words before and after a gap.
- Look at the answer options and choose the option that fits best.
- Look at the other options to check they are not correct.

Exam **TASK**

Multiple-choice cloze

For each question, choose the correct answer.

Passwords are important for keeping our information safe. We have to **(1)** _____ a password to use our email and other things on computers. We sometimes need one to use our **(2)** _____ phones when we want to **(3)** _____ a friend. We use passwords when we use social **(4)** _____ . But there is a problem with having a lot of passwords. People get tired of using them because they **(5)** _____ online many times a day. So, they want something easy to remember. Can you believe that a lot of people choose 1234567 for their password? Many services ask people to make strong passwords and use letters, numbers and special characters like @, & or *. They might be more difficult to remember, but it's the best way to stay safe **(6)** _____ .

1	A download	B enter		C send	
2	A social	B digital		C mobile	
3	A check	B call		C go	
4	A internet	B web		C media	
5	A go	B enter		C chat	
6	A online	B onscreen		C offline	

Grammar 1
present continuous for future plans and arrangements

1 Look at Fatima's diary and read sentences (1–6). Three of these sentences are incorrect. Find and correct the mistakes.

APRIL	
Monday 8th	Email Trisha
Tuesday 9th	Study for computer exam
Wednesday 10th	Write blog
Thursday 11th	Meet Isha
Friday 12th	Have dinner at Zehra's house
Saturday 13th	Visit Yusuf and Elif
Sunday 14th	Go cycling with Berat

1 Fatima is emailing Trisha on Monday. _____

2 She isn't writing her blog on Wednesday. _____

3 Berat and Fatima are going cycling on Sunday. _____

4 Isha and Fatima aren't meeting on Saturday. _____

5 Fatima is going swimming on Tuesday. _____

6 Fatima and Zehra aren't having dinner together on Friday. _____

2 Write questions for the answers. Use the present continuous form of the verbs.

1 A: _____
   (Katerina / meet / Andrea)
   B: No, she isn't.

2 A: _____
   (you / study / for the maths test)
   B: On Monday.

3 A: _____
   (people / go / to Carolina's party)
   B: About twenty.

4 A: _____
   (you / do / after school today)
   B: I'm going to the 3D cinema with Sara.

Listening
choosing the correct picture; multiple choice with picture options

1 Read the Exam Reminder. When you look at the pictures before you listen, what do you need to think about?

_____

Exam **REMINDER**

Choosing the correct picture
- Some exam tasks give you three pictures and ask you to listen and choose the correct one.
- Read each question and look at the three pictures: which words might you hear?
- For each question, how are the three pictures the same or different?

2 **3.1 ▶** Listen and complete the Exam Task.

Exam **TASK**

Multiple choice with picture options
For each question, choose the correct answer.

1 What is the man having a problem with?

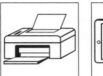

A   B   C

2 What time does the film start?

A   B   C

3 What did the boy buy online?

A   B   C

4 What are Rakesh and his friend doing this afternoon?

A   B   C

↻ Grammar Reference 3.1, p162 in Student's Book

Vocabulary 2 adjectives to describe technology

1 Write all the opposites of these adjectives that you can think of.

1 excellent _____

2 old _____

3 easy _____

4 boring _____

5 different _____

6 unusual _____

2 Complete the sentences with these words.

easy	interesting	normal	old
terrible	the same		

1 This computer is very _____ . My dad bought it years ago and it's quite slow!

2 Most mobile phones are _____ to use. You just turn them on and you can call friends or go online.

3 My computer class is so _____ . Now I like computers more than I did before.

4 This camera is _____ ! The photos are really dark.

5 That isn't a different DVD player. That's _____ one!

6 When you turn on a computer, it's _____ to wait a minute before it starts.

3 Complete the blog post with these words.

blog	careful	computers	difficult
downloads	internet	laptop	mobile phone
modern	normal	old	video

My aunt Gabriella is 82 years old and she used to say that she wasn't interested in learning how to use
[1] _____ . "I'm too [2] _____ for these
[3] _____ things," she used to say. Computers are too [4] _____ for me to understand. Then I moved to this country to study. She didn't have a
[5] _____ and, for a while, she called me on her [6] _____ phone, but it was very expensive. However, a month ago, her son, my cousin Ricky, gave her a [7] _____ , and so she discovered the [8] _____ . Now we see each other on a
[9] _____ call once a week and she tells me all about the results of her research – on everything! News, the place where I live, the place where she lives, history (two weeks ago she found a [10] _____ that talks about her father) – she even [11] _____ music now! I had to tell her to be [12] _____ !

4 Choose the correct words to complete the text.

The first computer was called ENIAC, and a group of scientists built it in the 1940s. It was much larger than the [1] ___ computers of today. The machine was [2] ___ because it filled a very large room. In fact, a [3] ___ two-bedroom home in the UK is half the size of this room. Can you imagine having a computer that's bigger than your house? It's really [4] ___ ! How did this computer work? It was not [5] ___ to use and several people used it at the same time. Also, it didn't have a screen or a printer. It put holes in paper cards, and people had to read the cards to get information. That sounds [6] ___ , doesn't it?

1 **A** old **B** modern **C** interesting

2 **A** excellent **B** unusual **C** boring

3 **A** different **B** normal **C** terrible

4 **A** old **B** careful **C** difficult

5 **A** easy **B** modern **C** excellent

6 **A** excellent **B** normal **C** terrible

5 Write sentences using adjectives to describe these things.

1 your mobile phone

_____

2 the web

_____

3 downloading files

_____

4 computer games

_____

5 social media

_____

6 technology lessons

_____

Grammar 2 prepositions; choosing the correct preposition; open cloze

1 Choose the correct words to complete the sentences.

1 Leo is *at / on / in* the cinema.
2 I was working on my laptop when my little brother jumped *to / at / onto* my bed.
3 Bill walked *at / towards / on* the printer to take his science homework.
4 Anna was excited when she walked *onto / on / into* the Technology Museum.
5 What did Ms Smith write *at / on / in* the board?
6 My tablet is *on / at / in* my bag.

2 Complete the sentences with at, on or in.

1 We always go to the beach _____ the summer.
2 My dad bought his first mobile phone _____ 2000.
3 The film is _____ 7 p.m.
4 The Technology Museum isn't open _____ the morning.
5 I wrote a post _____ 1st April.
6 I don't use social media _____ the weekend.
7 I don't like using my computer _____ night.
8 Our school exams are _____ June.

3 Look at the picture. Complete the text with these phrases.

| the bottom | the left | the middle |
| the right | the top | |

Natasha keeps her desk very tidy. She has her printer on ¹ _____ side of her desk. Her laptop is in ² _____ of her desk. She keeps her schoolbooks on ³ _____ side of her desk. Today she's writing an email to her friend Yuri. She puts Yuri's name at ⁴ _____ of the email. When she finishes the email, she puts her name at ⁵ _____ .

4 Complete the sentences with in, at or on and a day, a clock time, a time period or a place.

1 I live _____ .
2 I start school _____ .
3 I keep my schoolbooks _____ .
4 I do my homework _____ .
5 The school holidays are _____ .
6 My mobile phone is _____ .
7 I usually text my friends _____ .
8 I watch films _____ .

5 Read the Exam Reminder and complete the Exam Task.

Exam REMINDER

Choosing the correct preposition
- First, read the text quickly, to understand the general idea.
- Then read each sentence slowly. Look at the words around the gaps.
- Is a preposition missing? Is it a preposition of movement, time or place?
- Write a preposition, then read the sentence to check.

Exam TASK

Open cloze
For each question, write the correct answer. Write **one** word for each gap.

Hi Simon

Ahmad is coming here tomorrow
(1) _____ 2 p.m. to work on our science project. Do you want to come too? You remember where my house is, right? It's
(2) _____ the top of the hill
(3) _____ the right side of the street.
We can use the printer **(4)** _____ my sister's room and finish the project for the presentation **(5)** _____ Monday. We're going to the cinema after that. We can take the bus **(6)** _____ the stop around the corner. Is that okay?

Bye for now
Jessica

Grammar Reference 3.2, p162 and p163 in Student's Book

Writing
important information; checking your work; writing a note

1 Label the information with these words.

| address | date | email address | event |
| phone number | | time | |

1 0446 548865 _____
2 Tech Fair at Expo Centre _____
3 24 Westville Street _____
4 8.00 p.m. _____
5 14th June _____
6 expocentre@gomail.com _____

2 Read the poster and the email. Then choose the correct answers.

Shelby Tech Museum

Grand Opening

On Saturday 22nd May,
from 12 p.m. to 8 p.m.

Come and help us celebrate our opening!

FREE ENTRANCE

PRESENTATION
The History of Computers
by Museum Head Peter Langley

- Free food and drinks
- Interactive displays

For more information, visit www.shelbytechmuseum.com

Email Message

From: Bethany
To: John

Dear John

Do you want to go to the new Tech Museum's Grand Opening on Saturday? It sounds interesting and you love computers. It's on 141 Easton road in shelby city centre from twelve p.m. to 8 p.m. It takes twenty minutes to get there from your home.

Write back soon!

Bethany

1 You can find out where the museum is from the *poster / email*.
2 You can find out what event is taking place at the opening from the *poster / email*.
3 You can find out about other events *from the poster / by emailing the museum*.

3 Read the Exam Reminder. When do you need to use capital letters?

_____

4 Look again at the email in Exercise 2. Find two mistakes with capital letters and a mistake with a time. Correct the mistakes in the email.

5 Read and complete the Exam Task below. Don't forget to use the Useful Language on page 39 of your Student's Book.

Exam TASK

Writing a note

You are going to a comic book fair tomorrow. Write a note to your friend, Carmen.

In your note say:

- where you want to meet
- what time you want to meet
- what you want to do there.

Write **25 words** or more.

Reading reading for detail; multiple choice with one text

1 **Read the Exam Reminder. How can we understand a key word better?**

Reading for detail

- When a question asks about a detail in the text, underline the key word in the question.
- Read the text and find the key word, or words with the same meaning.
- When you find a key word, read the text before and after it. Make sure you understand the meaning.
- Look at the answer options for the question. Which is the best answer?

2 **Now read the text and complete the Exam Task.**

Multiple choice with one text

For each question, choose the correct answer.

1 The article is mainly about
  A growing plants with lights.
  B saving water.
  C a new way of growing food.

2 What problem do traditional farms have?
  A The farms are too small.
  B They can only sell one type of fruit and vegetable.
  C It can be difficult to find farm workers.

3 On vertical farms, where do the plants grow?
  A on shelves in big fields.
  B in special buildings.
  C in hot places.

4 Why do farmers look at photos of the plants?
  A to check when to change the lights
  B to check how healthy the plants are
  C to check that the plants always receive water

5 The article concludes that in the future people will
  A think more about nature.
  B stop eating meat.
  C only eat food from vertical farms.

The future of farms

Scientists believe that the number of people in the world – the population – will be about 10 billion by 2050. That's a lot of people! How will we have enough food for everyone to eat? There are some big problems with farms today. Traditional farms need a lot of land and use a lot of water, and this means many problems for nature. Plus, farmers can only grow food when it is the right time of the year, and they often grow just one kind of fruit or vegetable. And then it is not always easy to find farm workers to pick it when it is ready. People know that the way we grow food – and what we eat – needs to change. But how will this happen?

One idea is *vertical farming*. Instead of growing fruit and vegetables in large fields that need good weather and use a lot of water, scientists are making farms inside buildings. These farms grow fruit and vegetables on many shelves. Farmers put special lights near the plants. The lights aren't very hot, they don't need much electricity and farmers don't need to change them very often. The plants also receive water, but they only get the water that they need, when they need it. This is because cameras take photos of the plants. The photos go into computers that tell the farmers how well the plants are growing and how much light and water they need. All this means that farmers can grow more food in a short time and in good and bad weather.

Customers are going to become much more careful about the food that they buy in the future. People will probably eat less meat and they will want to choose food that is good for nature. Perhaps vertical farming will be the solution.

Vocabulary 1 food

1 Choose the correct words to complete the sentences.

1 I usually put a little *rice / lemon / butter* on my bread.

2 Do you like pizza with lots of *grapes / milk / cheese*?

3 *Oranges / Onions / Peppers* are my favourite fruit.

4 *Fish / Pasta / Garlic* with a tomato and mushroom sauce is a healthy carbohydrate for dinner.

5 I don't like *chillies / eggs / bananas* because they are spicy.

6 Miranda doesn't eat *salad / meat / potatoes*. She's a vegetarian.

2 Write a word from Exercise 1 next to each photo.

1 _____

2 _____

3 _____

4 _____

5 _____

6 _____

3 Write food words for the definitions.

1 This can be brown or white and we use it to make an omelette. **e** _ _

2 We use the juice of this yellow fruit with water and sugar to make a drink. It's really good when the weather is hot. **l** _ _ _ _

3 This vegetable has a strong taste. We add pieces of it when we cook food so it tastes good. **g** _ _ _ _ _

4 This vegetable can be green, red or yellow. We sometimes put it on a pizza. **p** _ _ _ _ _ _

5 This vegetable is brown or white and the top is round. Only some types are safe to eat. **m** _ _ _ _ _ _ _

6 This vegetable is red and we use it for many things. We can eat it fresh in a salad, or we can cook it and make a sauce. **t** _ _ _ _ _ _

4 Which food items need preparation before you buy them, which don't and which do people make from ingredients? Complete the table with these words.

butter	cheese	eggs	grapes	meat
milk	pasta	rice	tomatoes	

No preparation	Need preparation	From ingredients

5 Complete the coversations with the correct food items.

1 **A:** Are you OK? Why are you crying?

B: Don't worry. I'm just cutting these _____.

2 **A:** Is it OK if I put _____ in the tomato sauce?

B: Yes, I love spicy food!

3 **A:** I always have a piece of _____ at the end of a meal.

B: Me too. I love apples and bananas.

4 **A:** Do you like _____?

B: No, I don't like any type of seafood.

5 **A:** Here's your tea.

B: Thank you. Oh, you put _____ in it – I like it black. Are you sure this is for me?

6 **A:** How many _____ do we need to make the omelette?

B: Five. We also need some _____ or oil. Have we got any?

Grammar 1 be going to; will

1 **Complete the sentences with the correct form of** *be going to* **and the verbs.**

1 I _____ (do) the shopping this evening.

2 Ann _____ (make) dinner.

3 The pizza in that restaurant was terrible. We _____ (not eat) there again.

4 _____ (you / clean) the kitchen soon?

5 Rani _____ (not help) us prepare for the party. She's busy.

6 _____ (he / try) a new recipe?

2 **Choose the correct answers.**

1 I _____ do the shopping tomorrow. Can you come with me?

  a 'm going   **b** won't   **c** 'm going to

2 I think I _____ buy these lemons. They look quite nice.

  a 'm going to   **b** 'll   **c** 'm going

3 That pasta looks delicious. I'm sure everyone _____ love it!

  a 're going to   **b** 're going   **c** will

4 It's really hot here in the kitchen. I _____ open a window.

  a 'm going to   **b** 'll   **c** 'm going

5 Ebru just called. He and Yasmin _____ make a cake for Esra's birthday.

  a are going to   **b** 's going to   **c** will

6 In the future, I believe our food _____ healthier.

  a are going to be   **b** will   **c** will be

3 **Complete the conversations with** *be going to* **or** *will.*

1 **A:** I don't understand this sentence.

  B: Don't worry, I _____ help you.

2 **A:** I left my maths book at your house yesterday.

  B: Yes. I saw it. I _____ go out in twenty minutes. I can bring it to you.

3 **A:** I'm going to be late for basketball practice.

  B: OK, I _____ tell the coach.

4 **A:** I forgot to bring money for lunch.

  B: I _____ lend you some.

5 **A:** It's granny's birthday on Sunday and I don't know what to get her.

  B: I do. I _____ give her a sun hat.

Listening understanding what to listen for; multiple choice with one conversation

1 **Read the Exam Reminder. What do you need to find in the questions?**

_____

2 **4.1** ▶ **Listen and complete the Exam Task.**

Exam TASK

Multiple choice with one conversation

For each question, choose the correct answer.

You will hear Paloma talking to her friend Sebastian about cooking something together.

1 Paloma is going to make a cake with
  A strawberries and bananas.
  B chocolate and bananas.
  C lemons and cream.

2 When are Paloma and Sebastian meeting?
  A one o'clock
  B quarter past one
  C quarter to two

3 What is Paloma going to eat?
  A snacks
  B pizza
  C sandwiches

4 Paloma asked Sebastian for help because
  A he works in a restaurant.
  B his mum has a cake shop.
  C he makes cakes all the time.

5 How long does the cake need to cook?
  A twenty minutes
  B thirty-five minutes
  C about one hour

◀ ↻ **Grammar References 4.1, p163 and p164; 4.2, p164 in Student's Book**

Vocabulary 2 cooking and measurements

1 Complete the expressions with these verbs.

add	bake	make	mix	pre-heat
roll out				

1 _____ the oven
2 _____ a hot snack
3 _____ in the oven
4 _____ the eggs to the flour
5 _____ the ingredients together
6 _____ the dough

2 Match the first part of the sentences (1–7) with the second part of the sentences (a–g).

A simple, tasty lemon biscuit recipe!

1 First, cut 115 grams of butter _____ .
2 Then, put the butter with 200 grams of sugar in a bowl and _____ .
3 Next, add 1 large egg and 3 tablespoons of lemon juice _____ .
4 Add 245 grams of flour and ½ teaspoon of baking soda. Mix everything together _____ .
5 Preheat _____ .
6 Roll the dough _____ .
7 Bake for ten minutes _____ .

a with a large spoon
b into small round balls
c in the oven
d mix them together
e into small pieces with a knife
f the oven to 175° C
g to the butter and sugar

3 Choose the correct words to complete the sentences.

1 My cake was terrible! I forgot to *add* / *mix* the eggs to the dough.
2 Preheat the oven to 200 *grams* / *degrees* celsius.
3 You can cook many things in *an oven* / *a spoon*, such as pizza, cakes and biscuits.
4 You need to use *yoghurt* / *flour* to make cake and biscuit dough.
5 Each biscuit is about 5 *centimetres* / *kilometres* round.
6 You need around 200 *grams* / *kilos* of cheese to make this delicious omelette.

4 Write L (length), W (weight) or T (temperature) next to the measurements.

1 180° C _____
2 30 centimetres _____
3 200 grams _____
4 5 kilometres _____
5 1 kilo _____
6 10 metres _____

5 Complete the conversation with these words.

add	bake	centimetres	cut	grams
make	mix	pre-heat	roll	spoon

Aya: Lyn, can you show me how to [1] _____ your chocolate biscuits? I want my family to try them.

Lyn: Of course. They're really easy. You'll need 50 grams of butter, 50 grams of sugar, some flour, an orange and a little chocolate. Have you got them?

Aya: I think so. How much flour do I need?

Lyn: 120 [2] _____ .

Aya: OK. I've got everything we need.

Lyn: Great. So, first you need to [3] _____ the oven to 190° C. Then squeeze the orange and I'll cut the chocolate into pieces.

Aya: Okay. What do I do now?

Lyn: [4] _____ together the butter and sugar with a [5] _____ .

Aya: Like this?

Lyn: Yes, perfect. Now [6] _____ the flour, two spoons of orange juice and the pieces of chocolate. [7] _____ out the dough on a board and [8] _____ it into round shapes of four [9] _____ .

Aya: OK – how do they look?

Lyn: Great! Now let's [10] _____ them in the oven for 10 to 15 minutes.

Aya: That's great. You were right. They aren't difficult.

Grammar 2 countable and uncountable nouns; quantifiers

1 **Write C (countable) or U (uncountable) next to the words.**

1	rice	_____	11	cake	_____
2	biscuit	_____	12	equipment	_____
3	grape	_____	13	apple	_____
4	water	_____	14	information	_____
5	egg	_____	15	sugar	_____
6	cheese	_____	16	banana	_____
7	chocolate	_____	17	salt	_____
8	furniture	_____	18	traffic	_____
9	mushroom	_____	19	advice	_____
10	fruit	_____	20	chair	_____

2 **Circle the odd one out.**

1 news / maths / subjects
2 food / biscuit / dinner
3 lesson / homework / test
4 sugar / water / apple
5 child / boy / girl
6 furniture / equipment / bike

3 **Choose the correct answers.**

1 How _____ people are at the party?
  a a few   **b** many   **c** much

2 We might need _____ cheese and biscuits.
  a little   **b** few   **c** some

3 There isn't _____ coffee in the cupboard. I'll go to the shop and buy some.
  a any   **b** some   **c** many

4 Do you like _____ milk in your tea?
  a much   **b** lots of   **c** a few

5 We haven't got _____ time because the shops are closing soon.
  a many   **b** much   **c** a little

6 There are _____ bananas in the kitchen.
  a a little   **b** any   **c** a few

7 How _____ luggage are you taking with you?
  a many   **b** little   **c** much

8 I like _____ cheese on my pasta.
  a much   **b** a lot of   **c** many

9 Is there _____ yoghurt in the fridge?
  a any   **b** some   **c** many

10 I'm going to cook _____ rice for dinner.
  a a few   **b** any   **c** some

4 **Correct the mistakes in the sentences.**

1 Do you have any informations about cooking classes? _____

2 I'm reading book about vertical farms. Do you know anything about them? _____

3 Dad, I need some money to buy some snack for school. _____

4 We haven't got any foods for dinner. I'll go and buy something. _____

5 Our kitchen is small, so there isn't much furnitures. _____

6 Hank has dinner after he finishes his homeworks. _____

7 There were six child at the party, but only five chairs. _____

8 Maths and science are my two favourite subject. _____

5 **Complete the conversation with these words.**

any much	few some	little	lot	many

Andrej: What are we going to have for lunch? How about a pizza?

Milena: Well, we've got [1] _____ flour, but we haven't got [2] _____ cheese.

Andrej: Well, I can go to the supermarket. What else do we need?

Milena: Can you get a [3] _____ onions?

Andrej: OK. What about tomatoes for the sauce?

Milena: Yes, of course. I like a [4] _____ of sauce on my pizza.

Andrej: Me too. What else? Ham?

Milena: Yes, let's have ham.

Andrej: Great. How [5] _____ ham do you want on it?

Milena: Just a [6] _____ . And what about some chillies?

Andrej: How [7] _____ do we need?

Milena: Lots of those – I love them!

↻ **Grammar References 4.3 and 4.4, p164 in Student's Book**

Writing
using adjectives; using short forms, punctuation and greetings; writing an email

Learning REMINDER

Using adjectives
- Include adjectives when you are writing about past activities or future plans to make your writing more interesting.
- Use positive and negative adjectives to give your opinion (*it'll be great, it was boring*).
- For stronger opinions, use qualifiers such as *really, very* and *quite* (*it'll be very exciting, it was really fun*).

1 Write an adjective to describe these activities. Use the adjectives *boring, great, fun* and *exciting* and the adverbs *really, very* and *quite* if you like.

1 clean the house _____
2 go camping _____
3 see a play _____
4 do exercise _____
5 have a party _____
6 cook dinner _____

2 Read the Exam Reminder. Why should you use short forms in emails to friends?

_____

Exam REMINDER

Using short forms, punctuation and greetings
- Short forms are informal and you should use them when you write informal emails (for example, to a friend).
- Exclamation marks are also informal. You can use them in informal emails to show you are excited or annoyed about what you're writing about.
- When you write an email for an exam task, you should always use a short greeting at the start and sign off with your name at the end.

3 Read the writing task and choose the correct answer, a or b.

You are going camping with your brother this weekend. You want to invite your friend Oscar. Write an email to Oscar.

In your email:
- explain your plans for the weekend
- ask Oscar to come with you and say why it will be fun
- say when and how you will travel to the campsite.

Write **25 words** or more.

1 a You're going to email your brother.
   b You're going to email Oscar.
2 a You're going to ask Oscar how you'll travel.
   b You're going to ask Oscar to come with you.
3 a You're going to say how you're getting there.
   b You're going to say where the campsite is.

4 Read a student's answer to the writing task in Exercise 3. Find phrases you can write in short form and rewrite them.

Hi Oscar

I am going camping this weekend with my brother. Can you come? It is going to be great fun! My brother is going to cook burgers. We are going to leave at 10 a.m. on Saturday morning and drive to the campsite. Let me know what you think.

Helena

5 Read and complete the Exam Task. Don't forget to use the Useful Language on page 51 of your Student's Book.

Exam TASK

Writing an email
You are going to have a party at your house on Saturday, and you want your friend Haris to help you. Write an email to Haris.

In your email:
- say how you feel about the party
- ask Haris to help you prepare the food
- tell him what food you plan to make.

Write **25 words** or more.

Reading answering negative questions; multiple matching

Fantastic treehouses

Treehouses are every child's dream. It is so much fun to go up a tree and be in a little area that's all your own. The view is amazing, of course! It is quiet, calm and relaxing and you can be near nature. It's also a great place to spend time with your friends. Here are some interesting treehouses around the world.

Between Alder and Oak, Osnabrück, Germany

This treehouse sits between two different types of trees, an alder tree and an oak tree, in a forest in the Osnabrück area of Germany. The two trees grew in a 'V' shape, so it was a perfect place to build a treehouse! It's not a very big house. It's only got one room. The room has got a bed, and there are windows in most of the walls. The ceiling is round – that's unusual – and it's got a small window in the top. It's a great place to sleep, read books and enjoy nature. There is also heating, so the treehouse is very warm in winter.

Tree Dragon, Miyagi Prefecture, Japan

A few years ago, the Japanese town of Higashi Matsushima asked a company to help them build a new school – a treehouse. This became the 'Tree Dragon'. The treehouse has got stairs that go up three levels, and there are classrooms on each one. The building company asked children in the town to help build it because they wanted the children to experience nature. They certainly did! After some time, the children knew the names of the birds, flowers and animals and the names of the trees around the forest.

The Alnwick Garden Treehouse, Northumberland, UK

The Alnwick Garden Treehouse is in a very large park in the town of Alnwick. Many people visit the treehouse because it's a very large, fun building with trees all around it. Visitors can't stay here, but anyone can walk around and see its rooms. It's got a great view of the area, and people can climb up very high and walk on small bridges near the treehouse. The bridges go through the trees and over roads. There is also a restaurant at the top of the treehouse with delicious meals for both adults and children and trees growing through the floor!

Vocabulary 1 houses and parts of a house

1 Read the Exam Reminder. How can we make a negative question easier to answer?

_____

Exam REMINDER

Answering negative questions
- In multiple-matching exam tasks the verb in the question is sometimes negative, e.g. *Which house hasn't got a garage?*
- To make sure you select the correct answer, change the negative question into a yes/no question, e.g. *Has (House A) got a garage?*
- If the answer to the question is *yes*, then the answer is <u>not</u> House A.

2 Now read the text and complete the Exam Task.

Exam TASK

Multiple matching

For each question, choose the correct answer.

	Between Alder and Oak	Tree Dragon	The Alnwick Garden Treehouse
1 Which treehouse offers food for the whole family?	A	B	C
2 Which treehouse is a good place to stay when it's cold?	A	B	C
3 Which treehouse is a place for learning?	A	B	C
4 Which treehouse only has space for a few people?	A	B	C
5 Which treehouse did young people help to build?	A	B	C
6 Which treehouse has got a special kind of roof?	A	B	C
7 Which treehouse is not in a forest in the countryside?	A	B	C

1 Complete the sentences with words for parts of a house.

1 I like watching TV in the **l** _ _ _ _ _ **r** _ _ _ with my family.
2 My dad is making breakfast in the **k** _ _ _ _ _ _ right now. I'm really hungry!
3 My mum parks her car in the **g** _ _ _ _ _ when she comes home from work.
4 Can you open a **w** _ _ _ _ _ ? It's really hot in here.
5 We've got a **g** _ _ _ _ _ at the back of the house. The flowers are beautiful in summer.
6 We often have dinner at the big table in the **d** _ _ _ _ _ _ **r** _ _ _.

2 Complete the definitions with the parts of a house.

1 We sleep, do homework and listen to music in this room. _____
2 We go up these to get to a higher part of a house. _____
3 This part of the room is above our heads. _____
4 This part of the house is on the top. _____
5 We brush our teeth and have a shower in this room. _____
6 This is where you are when you open the door and walk in. _____
7 We open this to go from one room to another. _____
8 This is between two rooms or between the inside and the outside. _____

3 Complete the sentences with the parts of a house.

1 Turn the computer game off, go to your _____ and do your homework.
2 **A:** Where's Sergei?
   B: In the _____. He's making a cake.
3 There's water all over the floor in the _____! Who was the last to have a shower?
4 Can you help me put this picture on this _____?
5 It's an old house with very large rooms and very high _____. That's why it's always very cold there.
6 She fell when she was running down the _____.

4 Complete the sentence with your own ideas.

My favourite room in our house is the _____ because _____
_____.

Grammar 1 present perfect simple;
already, just, (not) yet, ever, never; for and since;
identifying what type of word is missing; open cloze

1 **Complete the sentences with the present perfect simple form of the verbs.**

1 We _____ (just / visit) Kenji. He looks really well.

2 My dad _____ (clean) the whole kitchen, even behind the fridge.

3 Anja _____ (not have) lunch in a treehouse restaurant.

4 _____ (you / ever / buy) something really expensive?

5 I _____ (never / visit) a houseboat before. It sounds cool.

2 **Complete the sentences with *for* or *since*.**

1 My brother has lived in Barcelona _____ 2015.

2 Edita has been at university _____ two years.

3 We haven't visited Andrea's house _____ March.

4 We have been in the kitchen _____ two hours!

3 **Read the Exam Reminder and complete the Exam Task.**

Exam **REMINDER**

Identifying what type of word is missing
- First, read the whole text.
- Look at each gap. What type of word do you need – a noun, a verb or a preposition?
- For each verb, check the subject. Is it singular or plural?

Exam **TASK**

Open cloze

For each question, write the correct answer. Write **one** word for each gap.

Hi Anthony

How are you? I'm staying with my aunt and uncle in New York City. They've got a great flat with an amazing view. I've **(1)** _____ seen a view like it before! I've been here **(2)** _____ the beginning of the month and my aunt and uncle **(3)** _____ taken me to see a few things. I've **(4)** _____ visited the Empire State Building and that was brilliant! I haven't seen any Broadway plays **(5)** _____ , but I really want to go to one. I **(6)** _____ been on the underground yet. I've heard that it's quite busy, but I'm looking forward to it!

Bye for now,
Jacob

Listening identifying details; matching

1 **Read the Exam Reminder. How many answers do you NOT need to use?**

_____

Exam **REMINDER**

Identifying details
- In the matching task, you must listen for details in a conversation.
- The question items are the words on the left. You hear them in the same order as the conversation.
- The answers are on the right. Match each question item with an answer.
- Listen and choose the best answer. Then listen again to check your answer.
- The speaker may talk about one answer option before they say the correct answer.
- The speakers may say all of the seven answer options, but you only need to use five of them.

2 **5.1 ▶ Listen and complete the Exam Task.**

Exam **TASK**

Matching

For each question, choose the correct answer.

You will hear Pedro talking to his friend Samira about helping in the house. Which place does each person help to look after?

People		Place
1 Samira	☐	A bathroom
2 Pedro	☐	B garden
3 Layla	☐	C living room
4 Sergio	☐	D bedroom
5 Jairo	☐	E garage
		F kitchen
		G dining room

↻ Grammar References 5.1, 5.2 and 5.3, p165 in Student's Book

Vocabulary 2 furniture; verbs with prepositions; multiple-choice cloze

1 **Choose the correct words to complete the sentences.**

1 This *mirror / desk* is so dirty; I can't even see myself!

2 I like sitting in the *shelf / armchair* and reading my favourite book.

3 We've got *towels / carpet* on our floor, so it's quite soft.

4 My mum bought some really nice soap. I put it in the *bookcase / shower*.

5 Tomas filled the *bath / lamp* with warm water.

6 Our bathroom needs a new *toilet / sofa*.

7 My hands are wet. Have you got a *curtain / towel*?

8 Those are lovely *curtains / paintings* you've got on your windows.

2 **Complete the sentences with the words you didn't use in Exercise 1.**

1 I love sitting on this _____ . It's really comfortable!

2 That _____ is full of books. There must be over one hundred!

3 Can you turn on the _____ , please? I can't see very well because it's a bit dark.

4 Can you put these books on the _____ in the living room?

5 Those are beautiful _____ on your wall. I love all the amazing colours.

6 I always keep my _____ tidy. I keep my schoolbooks on the right and my laptop on the left.

3 **Write five sentences to describe your living room.**

1 _____ .
2 _____ .
3 _____ .
4 _____ .
5 _____ .

4 **Read the Exam Reminder and complete the Exam Task.**

Exam REMINDER

Verbs with prepositions

- This task type tests vocabulary and which words go together, for example, which preposition goes after a verb.
- Read the text to understand the main idea.
- Look at the word after each gap. Is the word a preposition?
- Look at the answer options and decide which of the verbs goes with the preposition.

Exam TASK

Multiple-choice cloze

For each question, choose the correct answer.

The Uros people **(1)** _____ on some very unusual islands in the middle of Lake Titicaca in Peru. They built the islands from reeds, a special type of grass which grows in water. They **(2)** _____ fish in the lake and cook on open fires outside their houses. Their homes have modern technology and people can watch TV, **(3)** _____ to music on the island's local radio station and **(4)** _____ to each other on mobile phones. Tourists like visiting the islands and **(5)** _____ about the local culture. Visitors can also buy souvenirs and **(6)** _____ for a ride in a reed boat.

	A		B		C	
1	A	live	B	move	C	stay
2	A	pull	B	pick	C	catch
3	A	play	B	hear	C	listen
4	A	talk	B	say	C	hear
5	A	studying	B	looking	C	learning
6	A	travel	B	go	C	have

Grammar 2 possessives

1 Complete the sentences with the words + 's or '.

1 I feel bad because I broke my _____ (neighbour) lamp.

2 _____ (Juan) dog often plays in the garden.

3 These are the _____ (children) toys. They need to put them in the bedroom.

4 Do you know where the _____ (girls) books are?

5 What's your _____ (cat) name?

6 That's not my painting. That's _____ painting. (James)

2 Complete the table with the correct possessive adjectives and possessive pronouns.

Subject Pronouns	Possessive adjectives	Possessive pronouns
I		
you		
he		
she		
it		
we		
you		
they		

3 Complete the conversations with the correct possessive adjectives or possessive pronouns.

1 **A:** Which car is Michael's?
   B: That's _____ red car over there.

2 **A:** Is this your bag?
   B: No. _____ is on the shelf.

3 **A:** Anna, Ben, are these your tennis rackets?
   B: No, _____ are in the garage.

4 **A:** Are you going to buy that jumper?
   B: Yes. I want to give it to my mother for _____ birthday.

5 **A:** Is that my science book?
   B: No, I put _____ in the bookcase.

6 **A:** We have just got a new carpet. Isn't it lovely?
   B: Yes, it is. I'll take _____ shoes off so it will stay clean.

4 Choose the correct answers.

In northern Scandinavia, there is a group of people called the Sami. [1] _____ homes are known as *lavvus*. They look a little bit like the tents that we use for camping. The difference is that [2] _____ are much stronger than camping tents. They look much cooler too! The lavvu works well for the life of the Sami. Large families live in them and they move from place to place. The Sami follow the animals – reindeer – that [3] _____ look after, so they need a home that they can take with them.

The Sami build lavvus so that they don't get cold from the strong wind. In the past, they used animal skins to make the walls of a lavvu, so [4] _____ walls kept them very warm. Today, they don't often use animal skins for their tents. Their tents are more like [5] _____ modern tents. Of course, it gets very cold outside and the Sami make fires inside the lavvu. For this reason, [6] _____ got a hole at the top where the smoke can leave safely.

1	**A** Theirs	**B** They	**C** Their
2	**A** their	**B** his	**C** theirs
3	**A** he	**B** they	**C** their
4	**A** it	**B** it's	**C** its
5	**A** ours	**B** our	**C** we
6	**A** it's	**B** its	**C** it

⟳ Grammar Reference 5.4, p165 in Student's Book

Writing
reasons and results; planning how to connect your ideas; writing a story

Learning REMINDER

Reasons and results

We use the words **because** and **so** to talk about reasons and results.

- *Because* gives a reason: *They moved to a new house **because** their old house was very small.*
- *So* describes a result: *Their old house was very small, **so** they moved to a new house.*
- In sentences with *so*, remember to use a comma after the reason clause and before *so*.

1 Complete the sentences with *because* or *so*.

1 My bedroom didn't look very good, _____ I put some nice posters on the wall.

2 I don't like the living room _____ it's quite small and very dark.

3 I cleaned the mirror _____ it was very dirty and it was hard to see anything in it.

4 The books were all over the floor, _____ I picked them up and put them in the bookcase.

5 We're going to eat in the garden today _____ the weather is warm.

6 Our flat is on the eighth floor, _____ I always use the lift.

2 There are eight mistakes in this story. Find and correct the mistakes.

Last yesterday, my friend Tadeo and I moved some furniture in my bedroom so I wanted my room to look different. Luckily, the bed was very heavy and we couldn't move it, because I asked my dad to help us. The three of us pushed the bed really hard. It almost flew across the room and Tadeo fell down on the floor! We laughed a lot so it was really funny. I guess my dad is very strong! After, Tadeo and I moved the bookcase and my desk without dad so he wanted to go into town. At the end, we had fun and my bedroom looks great!

3 Read the Exam Reminder. What type of words do you need to tell a story well?

Exam REMINDER

Planning how to connect your ideas

- First, look carefully at the pictures. Who are the people? Where are they? What do they do? Why? Write short notes to plan the story.
- Think about what linking words you need to connect the story and explain reasons and results.
- Think of good ways to begin and to end the story.

4 Read and complete the Exam Task below. Don't forget to use the Useful Language on page 63 of your Student's Book.

Exam TASK

Writing a story

Look at the three pictures.

Write the story shown in the pictures.

Write **35 words** or more.

Reading the purpose of a text; multiple choice with six texts

1 Read the Exam Reminder. Which three questions can help you understand the purpose of a text?

_____

2 Now read the texts and complete the Exam Task.

Exam TASK

Multiple choice with six texts

For each question, choose the correct answer.

1

Tall Trees Cinema
Grand Opening
2nd March

Come and celebrate with us!

Film tickets – £2 off, drinks and snacks – half price

First show – 1 p.m.

- A Food and drinks have a discount.
- B Only tickets for the 1 p.m. show are on sale.
- C There is only one show that day.

2

Sean, I've gone to the supermarket … we haven't got any bread for sandwiches. It's 2.30 p.m. now. I'll be back in about 25–30 mins. Sorry for the wait! Jill

Why did Jill write this note?

- A to see if Sean can come to her house later
- B to let Sean know that she is out
- C to ask Sean to bring bread for sandwiches

3

The front entrance to the museum is closed.

Please use the South Entrance.

Thank you for your understanding.

- A The museum is closed at the moment.
- B There is another museum south of here.
- C You can enter the museum another way.

4

Would you like to see all the best sights of Rome in one easy tour?

Rome Tours offers the best walking experience in the historic centre! You will love our fun five-hour tours. The ticket price includes lunch.

Call 322 459321 for pricing and more information.

- A The walking tour is for a couple of hours.
- B Tourists have to pay extra for their lunch.
- C You can call the number to find out the price.

5

Euro Air Flight 227 from Dublin to Cologne on Thursday 27th February will not fly out. We are working hard to find another flight for you as soon as possible. We will send you a text when we have more information.

- A The flight from Dublin to Cologne is delayed.
- B There are no other flights from Dublin today.
- C A person will contact passengers with new information.

6

From: Donna

To: Dad

I wanted to send you a quick email to say that we are in Amsterdam. Our guest house is lovely, but the room is a bit small for a family of four. The children are happy, but there was a mistake and little Raquel doesn't have a bed to sleep in at the moment. The staff are going to bring another one. I can't wait to see the city! Speak later!

- A Only Donna and Raquel are staying in the room.
- B Workers from the guest house will come to the room later.
- C Raquel will not be able to sleep in that room.

Vocabulary 1 places in a town

1 Choose the correct words to complete the sentences.

1 Paulo went to the *post office / pharmacy* to buy some stamps.

2 My parents are going to the *college / bank* because they want to get some euros for our holiday.

3 I'm going to the *bookshop / library* to buy something by Agatha Christie. I don't know any of her books, but the films are great, so I'm curious about them.

4 My cousin is a nurse and he works in a *hospital / department store*.

5 My friends and I play basketball at the *supermarket / sports centre* every Wednesday afternoon.

2 Complete the sentences with the words you didn't use in Exercise 1.

1 I'm going to the _____ to get some medicine.

2 Gina visited a _____ to look at some clothes, a new desk, some gifts and a few other things.

3 After school, Juliana is planning to go to the local _____ to study science and maths.

4 We need cheese, milk, bread, bananas and pasta. We can get that at the _____ near my house.

5 I can't study here – it's too noisy. I'm going to the _____ .

3 Write the places in a town where you can do these things.

1 play basketball   _____
2 post a parcel   _____
3 buy a desk   _____
4 take some money out   _____
5 buy trainers   _____
6 buy rice   _____
7 read a book   _____
8 buy a book   _____
9 have an operation   _____
10 do a course to
   become a nurse   _____

4 Complete the text with these words.

bank	college	hospital	library
post office		sports centre	

Guntur had a lot of things to do on Monday. First, he went to the [1] _____ to send a postcard to his friend Suharto. Then he went to the [2] _____ to get some money. After that, he went to his morning classes at his [3] _____ . During the afternoon break, he went to the [4] _____ to pick up a book. After his afternoon classes finished, he met Setia at the [5] _____ to play badminton. He visited his uncle in [6] _____ in the evening. It was a busy day!

5 Complete the conversations with places in a town.

1 A: I'm going to the _____ . Do you need anything?

   B: Actually, yes. Could you get me some yoghurt, please? I haven't got any for my breakfast.

2 A: I want to send this birthday card to Selma. Do you know how much the stamp is?

   B: No, sorry. You'll need to go to the _____ and ask.

3 A: What did the doctor say?

   B: She ordered some medicine. I'll go to the _____ now and get it.

4 A: The _____ rang while you were having your shower.

   B: Please don't tell me they cancelled the swimming class again!

5 A: I can't find my _____ card! Can you see it?

   B: I think you put it in the book you borrowed.

6 A: Why isn't Grandad answering his phone?

   B: Because he's in _____ . Aunt Jemma took him there last night because he wasn't feeling well. He's fine, but they want to keep him there for a few days.

7 A: Are you going to go to _____ after you finish school?

   B: Yes. I want to study computer animation.

8 A: Shaniqua works in the _____ in the city centre.

   B: I know! I think she works in the clothes section.

Grammar 1 demonstratives; one and ones

1 Choose the correct answers.

1 Is there anyone sitting in _____ seat right here?
   a this **b** these **c** that

2 Look at _____ buildings over there. They're over eight hundred years old.
   a this **b** these **c** those

3 _____ bookshop here has great discounts.
   a This **b** These **c** Those

4 Do you know _____ girl across the street? I've seen her before, but I can't remember her name.
   a this **b** these **c** that

5 _____ students over there are on the same university course as me.
   a That **b** Those **c** These

6 Do you like _____ shoes? I think they make my feet look big.
   a this **b** those **c** these

2 Four of the sentences are incorrect. Find and correct the mistakes.

1 I don't like the pizza restaurant near my house, but I like the one across town. _____

2 My friends João and Leonor work in a library. It's the ones next to the college. _____

3 The only German language dictionaries in the shop are the one on that shelf. _____

4 That department store doesn't sell furniture, but the ones on Richmond Street does. _____

5 The pool at my local sports centre isn't very big. I prefer the one in the city centre. _____

6 That café doesn't sell sandwiches anymore, so I buy the one from the supermarket now. _____

3 Complete the conversation with *this*, *that*, *these*, *those*, *one* or *ones*.

Ali: Bea, have you got a minute? I need some advice for a school project.

Bea: The [1] _____ about the history of London?

Ali: No, I finished [2] _____ project last month. I have to give a talk about two Oxford colleges.

Bea: Which [3] _____? Magdalen? Balliol? Trinity?

Ali: Are you going to listen to me or not?

Bea: Sorry. Go ahead. It's just that I know a lot about [4] _____ topic.

Ali: That's why I'm asking you. So, I have to choose a new [5] _____ and one of the really old [6] _____ .

Bea: OK. Can you get me [7] _____ two books on the top shelf over there?

Ali: [8] _____ two?

Bea: No, the [9] _____ next to them. They'll be very useful.

Listening listening for days, times and numbers; gap fill

1 Read the Exam Reminder. How do you hear the number '0' in a conversation?

_____

2 6.1 ▶ Listen and complete the Exam Task.

Exam TASK

Gap fill

For each question, write the correct answer in the gap. Write **one word** or a **number** or a **date** or a **time**.

You will hear a recorded message with some information about a sports centre.

Bell Sports Centre	
Opening hours:	7 a.m. to **(1)** _____ p.m. daily
Address:	**(2)** _____ Shelton Road
Monthly fee:	Starts at **(3)** £ _____
Yoga class:	Begins on **(4)** _____ September
Contact:	For yoga class, phone **(5)** _____

↻ Grammar References 6.1 and 6.2, p166 in Student's Book

Vocabulary 2 tourism; sightseeing and entertainment; prepositions of movement

1 Choose the correct words to complete the sentences.

1 Let's stop at this *hotel / café* on the corner and have an ice cream.

2 The *cinema / bus station* in Athens has buses to many towns across the country.

3 I love this old *castle / museum*. Do you know who used to live here?

4 We're staying at a really nice *guest house / airport* on our holiday in Kyoto.

5 This *theatre / restaurant* is amazing. It's got the best chicken in the city!

2 Write the places you didn't use in Exercise 1 to say what places these people are talking about.

1 Students pay just £2 on Wednesdays, so we go and see a film every week. _____

2 We arrived four hours before our flight, but it wasn't too bad. _____

3 I didn't want to go, but it's actually quite interesting, especially the cooking equipment from hundreds and hundreds of years ago.

_____

4 I've never seen a play before, so I'm looking forward to seeing actors at work.

_____

5 It wasn't very expensive and the room was comfortable. _____

3 Complete the conversations with the correct places.

1 A: Hello. Could you please send a taxi to 45, Green Street, going to the _____ ?

B: Certainly. National or international flights?

2 A: Where should we take Mum and Dad for their anniversary?

B: I've heard the Indian _____ in South Street has a new chef and she's very good.

3 A: What time does the film start?

B: 8.15. Let's meet outside the _____ at 8. I've booked the tickets online.

4 A: Let's not spend a lot of money on a _____ room.

B: I agree. Ashok told me there's a nice little _____ across the river. The rooms are comfortable and the breakfast is great.

5 A: What do you want to do tomorrow? Not visit another museum, please!

B: OK, but I think we should visit the _____ . The website says it's over 1,500 years old, with secret doors to underground rooms.

4 Complete the sentences with these words.

across	along	into	over	past
through	under			

1 I think we're lost. The map says that Sandro's house is here, but I think we walked _____ it.

2 It's a nice day. Do you want to walk _____ the park and have lunch at the restaurant on the other side?

3 Can we go _____ the road and look at that new shop?

4 I saw all of Barcelona when our plane flew _____ the city. It was really amazing!

5 Hussein walked _____ the restaurant and asked the waiter for a table by the window.

6 We have to sail _____ the bridge to get to the other side of the lake.

7 Mansour walked _____ the path by the river.

5 Choose the correct answers.

Horacio: There's a new ¹ _____ in my area. I hear they've got great burgers. How about we try it?

Kyle: Sure, that sounds great. Where is it?

Horacio: It's close to my house. You just walk ² _____ the street, turn left, continue for about ten minutes and you're there.

Kyle: You know, it's almost lunchtime, so why don't we go today?

Horacio: That's a great idea. I'll text my parents to let them know.

Kyle: Is it OK if I invite my friend Nour? We're going to the ³ _____ this afternoon. We're working on a history project for school.

Horacio: Yes, of course. I know Nour. We had a class together last year. I walked ⁴ _____ her the other day outside the library, but I couldn't stop because I was late for my maths class.

Kyle: Great, then we can all go together. I'll call Nour, and then we can walk ⁵ _____ the park so we can meet her and walk to the restaurant together.

Horacio: That sounds great!

1	A cinema	B restaurant	C castle
2	A into	B under	C along
3	A museum	B guest house	C airport
4	A through	B over	C past
5	A into	B under	C across

Grammar 2 articles

1 Complete the sentences with these words. Use *the* or no article.

Africa	Amazon	Asia	Brazil	dinner	Egypt	evening	Himalayas	Italy
Lake Washington		London	Mali	moon	Nile	spaghetti	sun	United Kingdom	USA

1 _____ is a very long river in _____ and Sudan.

2 Earth is the third planet from _____ .

3 _____ are very tall mountains in _____ .

4 _____ is the capital of _____ .

5 _____ is a type of pasta from _____ .

6 _____ is a long river in _____ .

7 _____ is a large lake in _____ .

8 _____ is a country in _____ .

9 We can see _____ in the night sky.

10 In summer, we have _____ quite late in _____ .

2 There is one mistake in each sentence. Find and correct the mistake.

1 I'm learning to play a piano. _____

2 Is there an university in your town? _____

3 Tell Martin I'll be at the sports centre in a hour. _____

4 How many castles are there in the Wales? _____

5 We're having the breakfast in the hotel dining room. _____

6 A BBC makes some interesting TV programmes. _____

7 You can have a apple if you're hungry. _____

8 Have you ever been to Netherlands? _____

3 Complete the text with *a*, *an*, *the* or – (no article).

For my school trip this year, we visited Syrrako.
Syrrako is [1] _____ village in my country,
[2] _____ Greece, and it's up high in
[3] _____ Pindus Mountains. We went
there by bus and we stayed at [4] _____
hotel in town. [5] _____ hotel
was quite comfortable, and there were lots of
[6] _____ nice plants in the garden outside.

The village has [7] _____ beautiful
old buildings and there are walking paths in
[8] _____ area. It was [9] _____
warm weekend and [10] _____ sun was
shining, so we really enjoyed walking around. There is
also [11] _____ river between Syrrako and
another village, Kalarites. We learned some things
about [12] _____ river from our teacher.
It can be dangerous when it rains, so people in the
village have to be careful. I took [13] _____
photos while I was there and I showed them to
[14] _____ friends when I returned home.

⮌ Grammar Reference 6.3, p166 and p167 in Student's Book

Writing
adding and contrasting information; planning your answers; writing answers to three questions

Learning **REMINDER**

Adding and contrasting information

When we want to link ideas, opinions or facts, we use linking words.

- We can use *also* and *too* to add something.
  We use *also* before the main verb and after the verb *be*.
  *The museum has got a shop. It's **also** got a café.*
  We usually use *too* at the end of a sentence.
  *The museum has got a shop. It's got a café **too**.*
- We can use *but*, *however* and *although* to contrast ideas or facts.
  We usually use *but* in the middle of the sentence.
  *The hotel is comfortable, **but** it is expensive.*
  We use *however* + comma at the beginning of a sentence.
  *The hotel is comfortable. **However**, it is expensive.*
  We use *although* at the beginning or in the middle of a sentence, and with a comma between the clauses.
  ***Although** the hotel is comfortable, it is very expensive.*
  *The hotel is comfortable, **although** it is expensive.*

1 Complete the text with these linking words.

also	although	but	however	too

My favourite place to visit at the weekend is Central Park. I go there almost every weekend with my friends Jean-Paul and Sebastian. I like it because it's a beautiful area with lots of trees. It's ¹_____ got a lot of great bike paths, so there are a lot of cyclists in the park ² _____ . Last weekend, there was a bike competition, and the three of us joined it. ³ _____ none of us won a medal, we had a great time. Sebastian almost got third place, ⁴ _____ the other cyclists were too fast! We've decided to try again. ⁵ _____ , we'll have to wait six months because the competition is only twice a year.

2 Add a comma to each sentence so the punctuation is correct.

1 Although I enjoy going to the cinema it is quite expensive.

2 My city's park is lovely but it isn't close to my house.

3 My favourite place is a swimming pool. However I don't often go there.

4 The skating rink is very popular although it is quite small.

3 Match the questions (1–3) to the answers (a–c).

1 Where is your favourite place to watch films? How often do you go there? _____

2 What do you like about it and why? _____

3 Tell me about the last time you went there. _____

a I went to Franklin Cinema last weekend with my best friends Clara and Albert. We watched a great action film. I bought some popcorn and I shared it with Clara and Albert. We sat close to the screen, although Albert wanted to sit at the back. We really loved the film, so we talked about it a lot after we left the cinema.

b I really enjoy seeing films at the Franklin Cinema. I usually go there once or twice a month with my friends or family.

c I like this cinema because they've got really comfortable seats. The cinema is quite small. However, the screens are really big and the sound is also amazing!

4 Read the Exam Reminder. Which questions need longer answers?

_____

Exam **REMINDER**

Planning your answers

- You will need to answer three questions on the same topic. Read the questions carefully, then choose a topic you have a lot to say about.
- Write down the key words for each question.
- Make sure your answers match the questions. The first question is the easiest. You need to write longer answers to the other questions.

5 Complete the Exam Task. Don't forget to use the Useful Language on page 75 of your Student's Book.

Exam **TASK**

Write sentences to answer the questions.

1 What is your favourite place in your town? How often do you go there?

_____
_____

2 What do you like about it and why?

_____
_____
_____

3 Tell us about the last time you went there.

_____
_____
_____
_____

Reading looking for phrases with the same meaning; multiple matching

A passion for art

Susanna

I entered a drawing competition and I've just had some good news – I'm the winner! The judges loved my work – a picture of the moon. I often look at the night sky in my free time because I love the stars and the moon. It was difficult to get the picture right and I spent a long time drawing it. My picture is going to be in a magazine. I'm so excited!

Ari

My brother Isaac saw a drawing competition in a magazine and he told me about it. I had several pictures already because I love drawing in my free time. I often draw animals, like tigers, lions and horses. However, I decided to enter a picture of a dinosaur. My picture won third place – I got £50 and I was happy about that. I'm going to enter again next year and I'll try to draw my best picture ever.

Nikos

We've got an amazing castle in our town, and I decided to draw it for a competition in an art magazine. The prizes were an art book for third place and £60 for second place. For first place, they put your picture in their magazine. Although I really hoped to win the money, I was really pleased when I won! It was great to see my castle picture in a really cool magazine.

Vocabulary free-time activities

1 Read the Exam Reminder. What should you look for in the text?

_____

Exam REMINDER

Looking for phrases with the same meaning

- Underline the key words in the questions.
- There is often a noun or an adjective in a question that means the same as a phrase or sentence in the text. For example, _It was fun = We enjoyed doing it._
- Find phrases in the text that mean the same as key words in the question.

2 Now read the text and complete the Exam Task.

Exam TASK

Multiple matching

For each question, choose the correct answer.

	Susanna	Ari	Nikos
1 Who wanted to win cash?	A	B	C
2 Who drew their picture before the competition started?	A	B	C
3 Who chose to draw something in their area?	A	B	C
4 Who needed a lot of time to draw their picture?	A	B	C
5 Who didn't get the top prize in their competition?	A	B	C
6 Who drew something from one of their other hobbies?	A	B	C
7 Who talks about doing their competition again?	A	B	C

1 Match the descriptions (1–5) with the free-time activities (a–e).

1 We do this outside, and we sleep in tents under the stars. _____

2 For this, we use pencils to make pictures on a piece of paper. _____

3 To do this, we ride on something that's got two wheels, and we often go really fast. _____

4 To do this, we make sounds using our voices. _____

5 We use lots of colours for this, and we make forests and mountains, a person's face or a beautiful building. _____

a painting
b camping
c singing
d cycling
e drawing

2 Complete the conversation with these words.

chess	dance	music	photography

Angie: Look at this. The community centre has some really great summer courses for young people. They're all free. Look at their website.

Lucy: Oh, that's cool! I didn't know that. Let me see. Oh, wow – there's a course called 'How to take great pictures'. I've always wanted to learn more about [1] _____ . My dream is to work for National Geographic.

Angie: And look at all the [2] _____ classes: guitar, drums, saxophone … I'll join the guitar one.

Lucy: And what about this? I don't like going to the gym – it's so boring, but they do salsa classes! I really want to do that – I love [3] _____ .

Angie: Can you believe it? There's a programme on board games too! I've always wanted to learn how to play one of the difficult ones, like [4] _____ .

Lucy: Oh, yes – that is difficult to play well. Why don't we join it together?

Grammar 1 zero conditional; first conditional

1 Write sentences in the zero conditional with these words.

1 if / it / rain / at weekends / we / often / play / board games

_____

_____

2 when / Jenny / go / camping / she / usually / take / her MP3 player

_____

_____

3 if / Jeff / go / to a museum / he / always / visit / all the exhibitions

_____

_____

4 Karl / always / lose / when / he / play / chess with Dan

_____

_____

5 Kyle / not go / cycling / when / the weather / be / bad

_____

_____

6 I / always / feel / sad / if / I / listen / to that song

_____

_____

2 Complete the sentences using the first conditional form of the verbs.

1 If you _____ (buy) the puzzle,
I _____ (help) you do it.

2 If Aunt Jamila _____ (visit) us this weekend, we _____ (play) cards together.

3 I _____ (buy) a new board game if Dad _____ (give) me the money for it.

4 If Amadou and Aminata _____ (not get) here soon, we _____ (leave) without them.

5 Jaime _____ (save) us a seat at the theatre if we _____ (ask) him to.

6 If they _____ (not clean) this pool, I _____ (not swim) here again.

7 I _____ (make) you some sandwiches if you _____ (be) hungry.

8 Sheetal's mother _____ (be) worried if she _____ (not call) soon.

Listening listening for examples; matching

1 Read the Exam Reminder. When you listen to the conversation, will you always hear the words in the list?

_____

Exam REMINDER

Listening for examples

• This task has a conversation between people who know each other.

• You may hear an example of a word in the list. For example, *board games* is in the list, but you hear *chess*. *Chess* is an example of a board game.

• Look at the words in the list and think of examples of each word.

2 🔲7.1▶ Listen and complete the Exam Task.

Exam TASK

Matching

For each question, choose the correct answer.

You will hear Claudia talking to Gary about free-time activities that they and their friends do. What does each person do in their free time?

People		Free-time activities
1 Claudia	☐	A reading
2 Gary	☐	B playing games
3 Stacey	☐	C writing
4 Jim	☐	D playing music
5 Paul	☐	E making things
		F doing sport
		G collecting things

▷ Grammar References 7.1 and 7.2, p167 in Student's Book

Vocabulary 2 music; using prepositions; deciding which answers are wrong; multiple-choice cloze

1 Write the names of the instruments.

1 _____

2 _____

3 _____

4 _____

2 Complete the sentences with these words.

classical	hop	MP3	opera	piano
pop	radio			

1 My parents took me to the _____ . I didn't want to go, but, actually, I liked the story.

2 Can you turn on the _____ ? The news is on in five minutes.

3 On long car journeys, we always play _____ songs and we all sing together loudly.

4 My dad doesn't like _____ music by people like Mozart. He prefers hip _____ .

5 Do you listen to music on your _____ player or on your phone?

6 I'm learning to play the _____ .

3 Choose the correct words to complete the sentences.

1 Are you interested *at / to / in* writing songs? There's a school club for it.

2 I'm not a big fan *to / at / of* that band.

3 Everybody's crazy *about / in / for* him, but I don't like his films.

4 Which sport clubs are you involved *at / to / in* right now?

5 Paulo's really *for / into / in* skateboarding. He goes skateboarding almost every day.

6 Are you keen *at / in / on* disco music?

4 Read the Exam Reminder and complete the Exam Task.

Exam TASK

Multiple-choice cloze

For each question, choose the correct answer.

The Vegetable Orchestra

A group of musicians in Austria do some interesting things in their free **(1)** _____ . They play vegetables! Their band uses carrots, peppers, onions and even garlic to make many **(2)** _____ of instruments. The band started with four members, and now there are ten. They have played in about three hundred **(3)** _____ over the past twenty years. The band spends two hours **(4)** _____ new instruments for every show. They use almost fifty kilograms of vegetables every time, and each vegetable **(5)** _____ different when they play it. What do the band members do when they finish with the vegetables? They often **(6)** _____ them in water and make a soup!

1	A hour	B time	C moment
2	A varieties	B models	C types
3	A works	B shows	C acts
4	A making	B doing	C being
5	A hears	B sounds	C listens
6	A boil	B mix	C add

Grammar 2 verb patterns; writing the correct verb form; open cloze

1 **Complete the sentences with the -ing form or to + infinitive form of the verbs.**

1 I can't imagine _____ (draw) a picture of my whole village.

2 I promised _____ (go) running with Itzel tomorrow, but it's going to rain a lot.

3 Ayoob really enjoys _____ (make) models of aeroplanes.

4 Camilla decided _____ (work) as a nurse.

5 Ricardo hopes _____ (start) his guitar lessons next week.

6 Lisa avoids _____ (listen) to opera music.

2 **Complete the sentences with too or enough and the adjectives.**

1 We were _____ (tired) to have another game of chess. It's a difficult game.

2 My sister was eighteen yesterday, so now she's _____ (old) to have driving lessons.

3 I'm _____ (busy) to enter the music competition this year. I've got clubs after school every day.

4 Javier isn't in the school play. He's _____ (scared) to go on stage, so he's helping with the music instead.

5 It isn't _____ (quiet) to study at home. My brother has just started playing the drums.

6 It was _____ (wet) to go camping last weekend, so we stayed at home and played board games.

3 **Complete the sentences with the correct form of these verbs.**

draw	enter	finish	go	join	make
play	win				

1 I need _____ three paintings for the school exhibition. It's next week.

2 My friend Intan suggested _____ the theatre club on Monday afternoons.

3 It's difficult _____ chess really well.

4 Hande agreed _____ cycling with Lorenzo on Saturday morning.

5 Branca's team was pleased _____ the basketball match.

6 Liu really enjoys _____ cartoons.

7 Rosaura has practised a lot and is ready _____ the singing competition.

8 Lara likes _____ videos on her phone.

4 **Write answers for the questions. Use the correct form of the verbs. Add the missing words.**

1 A: Where are you going?
   B: I / go / to the park / meet / my friends
   _____

2 A: Have you got any plans for this evening?
   B: I / promise / look after / my baby sister
   _____

3 A: I'm going to stay at home all day and study.
   B: Really? I / not / can / imagine / do / that.
   _____

4 A: Do you want to play basketball with us?
   B: it / be / too hot / do / sport
   _____

5 A: Does your brother go to the same gym as you?
   B: No, he / not / be / old enough / join.
   _____

5 **Read the Exam Reminder and complete the Exam Task.**

Exam REMINDER

Writing the correct verb form

• In a gap fill, if the missing word is a verb, you need to choose the correct form.

• Check the word before each gap. Is it a verb or a preposition?

• If it's a verb, do we usually use to + infinitive or an -ing after it?

• If it's a preposition, we usually use an -ing after it.

Exam TASK

Open cloze

For each question, write the correct answer. Write **one** word for each gap.

Hi Oscar

How are things? Are you enjoying your robotics club?

I've stopped **(1)** _____ to basketball practice. Maybe I'm just too old **(2)** _____ start now. I've decided **(3)** _____ do photography instead. I love **(4)** _____ photos of all sorts of things. I hope to **(5)** _____ a lot of new things about cameras, black and white photos and things like that.

Don't forget to **(6)** _____ me photos of the concert.

Stephen

↻ Grammar Reference 7.3, p167 in Student's Book

Writing expressing opinions; planning your ideas; writing an email

Learning REMINDER

Expressing opinions

- Use phrases such as *I believe…*, *In my opinion …* and *I think that …* to show that you are expressing an opinion and not giving a fact.
- Use phrases such as *I'm convinced that …*, *I strongly believe that …* and *I'm sure that …* to express a strong opinion.

1 Complete the sentences with these words.

believe	convinced	opinion
strongly	that	

1 I _____ that it will be really interesting to learn how to draw cartoons.

2 In my _____ , playing the violin seems very difficult.

3 I _____ believe that having hobbies helps you to feel happy.

4 I'm _____ that dance lessons are a great way to exercise.

5 I'm sure _____ you will learn a lot in your guitar lessons.

2 Read the email. What two activities is Taib interested in doing?

_____

Email Message
From: Taib
To: Marcos

Hi Marcos

How's it going? I want to tell you about some school clubs. I'm not sure which one to do. There is a robotics club that I'd like to join. The good thing about it is that you can learn how to plan, design and build a robot, and that seems fun! However, it's on Thursdays, and I'm busy on Thursdays: I've got basketball practice three days a week. I don't think that I can miss one day. I could also start piano lessons. On the one hand, piano music is beautiful and I'm sure that the lessons will be interesting. On the other hand, it's difficult and you need to practise a lot, and I'm not sure that I'll have the time. What do you think?

Taib

3 Read the email in Exercise 2 again and answer the questions.

1 What adjectives does Taib use in his email?

_____

2 What phrases does Taib use to begin his opinions?

_____

3 What phrases does Taib use to contrast ideas?

_____

4 What question does Taib use to ask for advice?

_____

4 Read the Exam Reminder. What do you need to include when you express your opinion?

_____

Exam REMINDER

Planning your ideas

- Read the task and underline the key words.
- Think of the opinions or advice you want to express in each part of the task.
- Think of adjectives to express your opinion and reasons to support them.
- Make brief notes about your ideas before you begin writing.

5 Complete the Exam Task. Don't forget to use the Useful Language on page 87 of your Student's Book.

Exam TASK

Writing an email

You are interested in joining an orchestra because you play the violin. However, you saw an advert for a skateboarding club, and you think that it may be more fun. Write an email to your friend.

In your email:

- tell your friend about the activities you want to do
- talk about a good and bad point of each activity
- ask your friend for some advice.

Write **25 words** or more.

Reading
checking the answer options; multiple choice with six texts

1 Read the Exam Reminder. What do you need to check when you look at the answer options?

a which option has the same words as the text

b what the main purpose of each option is

c which option means the same as the text

2 Now read the texts and complete the Exam Task.

Exam REMINDER

Checking the answer options
- Read all the texts. Where would you see them?
- What is the purpose or main message of each text?
- Read the answer options. What does each one mean? Does it mean the same as the text or does it mean something different?

Exam TASK

Multiple choice with six texts

For each question, choose the correct answer.

1

For Sale

Adult snowboard and helmet – £40

Two-year-old snowboard – looks great, but needs a small new part.

Call George on 03451 349876

A The seller is selling one piece of equipment.

B There is a problem with the equipment.

C The equipment is for children.

2

Sasha

Beth called – she'll be late for your swimming class at the sports centre. Don't wait for her, she'll just join you when she gets there.

Kate

A Beth and Sasha will be in the class together.

B Sasha needs to tell the class to wait for Beth.

C Beth will not be going to the swimming class.

3

IMPORTANT

Please do not run or push others in the pool area.

A You cannot be in this area.

B You need to walk slowly here.

C You can push people into the pool.

4

Hey Rodrigo, there's been a change for our Tuesday football practice. We're meeting at the park instead of the school field. Still at 5pm. See you then, Frank.

A Football practice is on a different day.

B Football practice is in a different place.

C Football practice is at a different time.

5

LOST – black sports watch.

Last seen at the badminton court on Friday 14th April.

Please contact Orlando on 02345 938211

Why did Orlando write this notice?

A to invite others to play badminton

B to find something that belongs to him

C to talk about a match on Friday

6

Green Hills Sports Centre

is offering weekend swimming lessons for children between the ages of five and eight. Notice to parents: the first ten children get 20% off.

A Lessons are from Monday to Friday.

B Both parents and kids can learn to swim.

C People who join early can get a discount.

Vocabulary 1 sport; sports equipment; sports people

1 Cross out the equipment that we do NOT use for these sports.

1	badminton	ball	racket	club
2	snowboarding	snowboard	bike	ball
3	volleyball	bat	ball	racket
4	rugby	ball	snowboard	bat
5	cricket	bat	club	ball
6	golf	bike	racket	club

2 Complete the table with these words.

basketball   baseball   cycling   football   golf
rugby   sailing   skiing   snowboarding
surfing   swimming   volleyball

Go	Play

3 Use a dictionary and find the meaning of the words in the box you don't know. Then use them to complete the sentences.

course   court   doubles   field   match
pitch   relay   singles   track   water

1 Swimming, surfing and sailing are _____ sports.

2 A _____ match is a tennis match with two players.

3 A _____ match is a tennis match with four players.

4 You play baseball and cricket on a _____ .

5 You play basketball and tennis on a _____ .

6 You can take part in a _____ in swimming and running.

7 You play golf on a _____ .

8 You play football and rugby on a _____ .

9 You play a football or rugby _____ , but a baseball game.

10 You can run on the road or on a _____ .

4 Choose the correct words to complete the sentences.

1 I really like my football *fan / player / coach* a lot. She helps us to be a good team.

2 Laila's an excellent football player and she's got a lot of *members / winners / fans* who really love her.

3 How many *players / fans / winners* are there on a cricket team?

4 Do you prefer individual or *member / fan / team* sports?

5 Are you a *player / member / winner* of any sports clubs?

6 Amy was the *member / player / winner* of last year's swimming competition.

5 Complete the text with words for sport, sports equipment and sports people.

There are no sports centres where I live, so last year my friends Samira, Jim and I decided to form a ¹_____ club. You can do it on the road, so you don't need a ²_____ to train on. Also, you don't need a lot of ³_____ – only a pair of good trainers. Jim's aunt knows a lot about running, so we asked her to be our ⁴_____ and she said yes.

At first, it was just the four of us. We trained every day before going to school, and we became good enough to enter competitions. Samira ⁵_____ the silver medal in the first one we did, and the local newspaper wrote about her. Also, people saw us training in the park and asked to join us. Now we have more than twenty ⁶_____ , and a local shop offered to support us and bought us uniforms. We even have lots of ⁷_____ who follow us to every event! We had nothing and we created something with the support of our community – that's real team work!

Grammar 1 modals of obligation and necessity

1 Choose the correct words to complete the sentences.

| Home | Information | Events | How to find us |

Welcome to
East Oak Riding Club

- Everybody is welcome. If you volunteer to feed the horses or work at our café, you [1] *have to / don't have to* pay for the lessons – it's all free!
- You [2] *don't have to / must* buy your own boots and helmet because we've got everything here.
- Before you get on the horse, you [3] *must / don't have to* check that the riding equipment is on correctly.
- You [4] *must / needn't* worry about checking the equipment alone. Someone will help you with it.
- You [5] *mustn't / have to* stay on the horse paths. You [6] *needn't / mustn't* leave the paths because it isn't safe.
- You [7] *don't have to / mustn't* give the horses any food.
- You [8] *needn't / must* return your boots and helmet at the end of the lesson.

Join us soon or click **here** for more information.

2 Complete the sentences with these words.

| don't have | has | have | must | must |
| mustn't | needn't | | | |

1 The last day to enter the competition is Saturday, so you _____ do it before then.

2 The match starts at 6 p.m., so we _____ be there before 5 p.m.

3 Mateo _____ to train really hard if he wants to win.

4 We _____ eat a big meal right before swimming.

5 It will be quite warm today, so you _____ to bring your jacket.

6 Allie _____ wear the right kind of boots when she goes hiking.

7 Do I _____ to go to the baseball game? I hate baseball!

Listening listening for numbers, dates and prices; gap fill

1 Read the Exam Reminder. How do we write the numbers 1, 2 and 3 in dates?

Exam REMINDER

Listening for numbers, dates and prices
- Listen carefully. Numbers ending in -*teen* and -*ty* (like *thirteen* and *thirty*) may sound similar.
- Check that your answer makes sense. For example, *30th February* is never correct, so the speaker probably said *13th February*.
- The ordinal numbers for *1*, *2* and *3* are *1st* (*first*), *2nd* (*second*) and *3rd* (*third*).
- There are three ways to say prices. For example, for *£21.30* we can say: *twenty-one pounds and thirty pence*, or *twenty-one pounds thirty*, or *twenty-one thirty*.

2 **8.1** ▶ Listen and complete the Exam Task.

Exam TASK

Gap fill

For each question, write the correct answer in the gap. Write **one word** or a **number** or a **date** or a **time**.

You will hear a woman giving a presentation about hockey lessons.

Fall Creek Sports Centre: hockey lessons

First class:	On the (1) _____ of next month.
Number of players:	Up to (2) _____
Age:	Must be at least (3) _____
Fee:	(4) £ _____ for a five-week course.
Contact:	Call (5) _____ .

◀ ↻ Grammar Reference 8.1, p168 in Student's Book

Vocabulary 2 parts of the body; health problems

1 Write the parts of the body in the correct order from the top of the body to bottom of the body.

arms	eyes	feet	fingers	hands
legs	neck			

1 _____
2 _____
3 _____
4 _____
5 _____
6 _____
7 _____

2 Complete the phrases for health problems with these words.

break	feel	go to	have	hurt

1 _____ a headache / a cold / a temperature
2 _____ your leg / your arm / your finger
3 _____ your foot / your eye / your neck
4 _____ hospital / the doctor's
5 _____ sick / tired / ill

3 Choose the correct words to complete the sentences.

1 Mr da Silva, I don't *have / feel* well. I think I need to go home.
2 Paul *felt / broke* his nose, so he had to go to hospital.
3 Lisa *broke / cut* her hand with a knife. She held a towel on it for a few minutes.
4 If we fall when we ride our bikes, we may *hit / feel* our heads, so we must wear helmets.
5 I think I *take / have* a temperature. My face feels very warm.
6 Those boxes are very heavy. I'll help you, so you don't *hurt / cut* your back.

4 Each of these people have got something wrong with them. Choose the correct answers.

1 Denny ate something bad for dinner. Now he's got _____.
   a a cold   b a headache   c a stomach ache
2 If Donna can't hear very well, she may have a problem with her _____.
   a nose   b ears   c eyes
3 Vincente went out on his bike in the rain. Now he doesn't feel well at all. He may have a _____.
   a cold   b toothache   c broken bone
4 Christina was sleeping on the sofa with her head up in a bad position. Now her _____ hurts.
   a neck   b eye   c nose
5 Tom went on a 10 km fun run yesterday. Now it's hard for him to walk! His _____ are really tired.
   a hands   b legs   c arms
6 When Helga looks at her computer screen for hours, her _____ hurt.
   a fingers   b hands   c eyes

5 Complete the story with these words.

ambulance	doctor	go to	hospital
hurt	leg	medicine	tired

Last summer we went to stay with my aunt and uncle in the countryside, but I had an accident and I spent the rest of my school holidays in bed. I was running down a hill and I fell over. I broke my left [1]_____ and I [2]_____ my neck. I was lucky the problem with my neck wasn't too bad. But when it happened I couldn't move, so my parents called an [3]_____ and it took me to [4]_____ . I was a bit scared, but the [5]_____ who helped me was really friendly and kind. She gave me some [6]_____ to stop the pain, and I felt really [7]_____ and sleepy after taking it. I got better and after four days my parents took me back home. The rest of the holiday was really boring for me and when I got home, I had to [8]_____ the doctor's a few times to make sure everything was OK with my leg and my neck.

Grammar 2 *can, could* and *may; should / shouldn't*

1 **Correct the mistakes in these sentences.**

1 You can't running in the school building.

   _____

2 I may use your snowboard this weekend?

   _____

3 We could have a rest? I'm really tired.

   _____

4 May I borrowing your football boots?

   _____

5 Could Jason coming over to play basketball?

   _____

6 Manuela and Maria-José can spend the night?

   _____

2 **Write sentences with these words and the correct modal for the prompts in brackets. More than one answer is possible.**

1 I / watch / the match on Sunday? (ask for permission, not formal)

   _____

2 I / borrow / your badminton racket? (ask for permission, formal)

   _____

3 they / practise / volleyball every day (give advice)

   _____

4 I / join / the chess club? (ask for advice)

   _____

5 you / go in / the pool today (say no to a request)

   _____

6 you / carry / my baseball bat for me? (make a request, not formal)

   _____

3 **Write a question for these situations.**

1 You want to borrow your friend's bike helmet.

   _____

2 You need to leave football practice ten minutes early.

   _____

3 You want advice about buying new trainers.

   _____

4 You want your sister to help you with your maths homework.

   _____

4 **Complete the conversations with *should / shouldn't* and a verb.**

1 **A:** I want to learn how to play badminton.

   B: You _____ a badminton class.

2 **A:** I went for my first run today. My legs really hurt!

   B: You _____ so much in the beginning. Just start slowly.

3 **A:** Joaquin fell and hurt his foot.

   B: He _____ to hospital straight away.

4 **A:** My eyes hurt from looking at the computer screen.

   B: You _____ at the screen for a long time.

5 **A:** I think we're playing cricket tomorrow at 4 p.m., but I can't remember.

   B: You _____ Jim and ask – I'm sure he knows.

6 **A:** I love this dress. _____

   B: No, you _____ . It's too expensive.

⟳ **Grammar References 8.2 and 8.3, p168 in Student's Book**

Writing
describing an event; using the correct tense; making notes; writing an article

1 Complete the sentences with the correct form of the verbs.

1 Amy and I _____ (decide) to go to a tennis match last weekend.

2 I _____ (look) forward to the match because I love tennis.

3 We _____ (arrive) at the match and we _____ (sit) down near the front.

4 While we _____ (wait) for the match to start, the players _____ (practise) and people around us _____ (take) photos.

5 It _____ (be) very exciting when the match _____ (begin). Everyone _____ (stop) taking photos and we all _____ (watch) the match closely.

6 Ella, my favourite player, _____ (do) well. Then she _____ (fall) and she _____ (hurt) her leg.

7 In the end, Ella _____ (lose), but Amy and I still _____ (enjoy) the match.

2 Complete the description with these adjectives and adverbs.

brilliantly	careful	difficult	excellent
excited	happy	quickly	suddenly

Yesterday we had a school football match, so my teammates and I met on the football field. We were really [1] _____ because it was the first match this year. Our coach, Mr Ribeiro, is an [2] _____ teacher and before the match started he told us we should be very [3] _____ because the other team is very good. At the beginning of the match, the other team played [4] _____ , but then we [5] _____ got the ball and we [6] _____ improved. It was a [7] _____ match, but in the end we won. We were all really [8] _____ !

3 Read the Exam Reminder. Why is it best to write very short notes?

_____

4 Read these notes about the opening of a new sports centre and number them in the best order.

A They opened, we went in ☐

B Went yesterday ☐

C Swimming pool better, gym, great equipment ☐

D Speeches first outside ☐

E Is where old sports centre was ☐

5 Complete the Exam Task. Don't forget to use the Useful Language on page 99 of your Student's Book.

Exam TASK

Writing an article
You recently visited a new shopping centre. Write an article (70–100 words) about your experience. You should:
- describe the centre, say where it is and what happened
- tell your readers what you enjoyed and didn't enjoy about the centre.

You should plan your article before you begin writing. Think about what you are going to write and make some notes to help before you start.

Reading
dealing with unfamiliar words; multiple matching

1 Read the Exam Reminder. What should you do after you find and underline the words you don't know?

_____

Exam **REMINDER**

Dealing with unfamiliar words

- Read the questions. What information do you need to look for?
- Then read all the texts.
- Underline the words you don't understand. Try to guess the meaning of each word from the sentence or the general meaning of the text.

2 Now read the texts and complete the Exam Task.

Exam **TASK**

Multiple matching

For each question, choose the correct answer.

	Martin Nittala	Becca Skinner	Nico Daniels
1 Who is hardly ever at home?	A	B	C
2 Who uses technology to change their photos?	A	B	C
3 Who started taking photos at the youngest age?	A	B	C
4 Who did something difficult with a child?	A	B	C
5 Who took photos inside their home?	A	B	C
6 Who works as a photographer?	A	B	C
7 Who sometimes takes photos of other people's homes?	A	B	C

Young photographers

Nico Daniels

Nico Daniels

Nico Daniels is a young photographer from Houston, USA. He started taking pictures with a camera he got for his eleventh birthday. Over the years, he saved money to buy a really nice camera. When he was fifteen years old, he decided to do a photography project in his brother's old bedroom. He asked friends to sit for the photos, and they wore beautiful red clothes. Then he added blue and purple lights behind them and, with all the different colours, his photos looked like wonderful dreams.

Becca Skinner

Becca Skinner is American and became interested in photography when she was at university. Nature is her passion, and she became a photojournalist and an outdoor adventurer. She spends a lot of her time travelling and sleeping in her truck. She often takes photos of remote places of great natural beauty. Once she went on a climbing and camping trip in the mountains with her best friend and her friend's son, who was then fourteen months old. You can see her photos on the National Geographic website and in magazines.

Martin Nittala

Martin Nittala is a young photographer from Rajahmundry, India. At fifteen he started taking photos with his brother's mobile phone. He loved it so much that he soon bought a camera to take better photos. With his computer, Martin adds colourful butterflies or bright lights to photos to make them more interesting. He takes many photos in the city streets. He might take a photo of an old bus, or a bird in a tree, or the evening sun over apartment buildings – each photo is beautiful in its own way.

Vocabulary 1 jobs; choosing the correct verb; multiple-choice cloze

1 **What do these people do? Write their jobs.**

1 _____

2 _____

3 _____

4 _____

5 _____

6 _____

2 **Complete the conversations with these words.**

engineer	journalist	nurse	police officer
receptionist	shop assistant		

1 **A:** What does your mum do, Yousef?
   B: She's a(n) _____ . She designs bridges.

2 **A:** A man just stole something from that bag.
   B: We should tell a _____ immediately.

3 **A:** What's your dad's job, Eleni?
   B: He's a _____ and writes for a newspaper.

4 **A:** Did you call the hotel about our room, Devin?
   B: Yes, I spoke to the _____ . He was very helpful.

5 **A:** There are so many phones to choose from! I don't know which one to buy.
   B: We should ask a _____ to help us.

6 **A:** I've hurt my arm and I think it's broken.
   B: Please sit over there – a _____ will be with you to take your details first.

3 **Choose the correct words to complete the sentences.**

1 Do you *take / earn / work* a lot of money in your job?

2 I'm going to *give / make / earn* a presentation about travelling safely.

3 My father used to work *in / on / to* a factory.

4 Do you have to *give / make / wear* a uniform at work?

5 I want to work *for / on / as* a software company.

6 Would you like to work *at / as / in* a nurse?

4 **Read the Exam Reminder and complete the Exam Task.**

Exam REMINDER

Choosing the correct verb
- To help you decide which verb goes in the gap, look at the word after the gap.
- Is it the object of the verb? e.g. *She ___ **her job**. (object); We ___ **early**. (not an object). Which verbs take an object and which don't?
- Is it a preposition? e.g. *I ___ **to** Sue*. Which verbs take that preposition?
- Is it *to* + infinitive, infinitive or *-ing*? e.g. *Don't ___ **to call** me* or *I ___ **playing** chess*. Which verbs take *to* + *infinitive*? Which verbs take *-ing*?

Exam TASK

Multiple-choice cloze

For each question, choose the correct answer.

Castle jobs!

What do you think is the best job ever? How about **(1)** _____ in a castle? There are many castles in Scotland which need people to **(2)** _____ lots of different jobs. It's also a great way to **(3)** _____ about Scottish history. You need different skills for each job. You may need to **(4)** _____ after the gardens or show people where they can park their cars. For castles that are in the **(5)** _____ of lakes, you may need to drive a small boat. You may also **(6)** _____ to tourists who visit the castle. Does it sound interesting? Have a look at our website to find out more.

1	A doing	B working	C earning
2	A do	B earn	C give
3	A study	B understand	C learn
4	A look	B watch	C see
5	A top	B bottom	C middle
6	A talk	B say	C tell

Grammar 1 relative pronouns

1 Combine the sentences using relative pronouns. More than one answer is possible.

1 I know a farmer. He lives in my village.

_____

_____

2 My mum works in a factory. The factory makes cars.

_____

_____

3 That's the man. He helped me when I lost my keys.

_____

_____

4 Priya saw a famous journalist. The journalist works for *The Times*.

_____

_____

5 Layla made a cake. It's on the table.

_____

_____

6 She scored a goal. It won the match.

_____

_____

2 Complete the text with *who*, *which*, *that* or *–*. More than one answer is possible.

Jack Randall is an adventure lover [1] _____ works with wild animals. He's a *zoologist*, which means he's a person [2] _____ studies and works with animals. He has a passion for reptiles – animals [3] _____ are born from eggs and have a hard skin, like snakes, turtles or, in the past, dinosaurs. He makes videos about snakes and other animals [4] _____ people are often afraid of, and he puts them on YouTube every week. He also visits places [5] _____ are difficult to get to, such as the deserts in Australia's Northern Territory. He loves filming the animals [6] _____ people don't often see.

Listening words that show a change; multiple choice with picture options

1 Read the Exam Reminder. In a conversation, what words do speakers use to show a change?

_____

2 **9.1** ▶ Listen and complete the Exam Task.

Exam TASK

Multiple-choice with picture options
For each question, choose the correct answer.

1 Where does Yolanda's brother work?

A   B   C

2 When does Abraham's new job start?

6th April	**13th April**	**14th April**
A	B	C

3 How much did Grigor pay for his laptop?

£450	**£500**	**£650**
A	B	C

4 What time should Francesca call again?

6:00	6:30	6:45
A	B	C

5 What is the woman's job?

A   B   C

▶ Grammar Reference 9.1, p168 in Student's Book

Vocabulary 2 school subjects

1 Complete the conversations with these school subjects.

art   biology   drama   geography
history   maths

1 **A:** What did you learn in _____ today, Malcolm?

B: We watched a video about what London was like in the 1700s.

2 **A:** What's your favourite subject, Aryan?

B: _____ . I love learning about the world and other countries.

3 **A:** Why do you like _____ so much, Lina?

B: I don't know. I just think numbers are really cool.

4 **A:** That's a lovely painting, Anton. Where did you learn how to paint like that?

B: I learned in my _____ class at school.

5 **A:** What things do you do in your _____ lessons with Mr Fernandez?

B: We study plays and we learn how to act out scenes.

6 **A:** I just love plants and animals. I think I want to be a vet or a zoologist.

B: Well, you must really like _____ lessons.

2 Write the school subjects.

1 _____

2 _____

3 _____

4 _____

3 Complete the sentences with these words.

exam   information   instructions   mark
project   question   subject   university

1 I'm so happy! I passed my biology _____ !

2 If you don't follow the _____ correctly, the machine won't work.

3 I'm sorry, I forgot to answer your _____ .

4 I hope to go to a good _____ after I finish school.

5 I didn't get a good _____ in my exam. I'll have to spend more time studying next time.

6 What school _____ do you prefer – maths or history?

7 You can get _____ about a lot of different things at a library.

8 Can we meet at my house to do our _____ for art class?

4 Complete the text with the correct verbs. Use the present simple or the past simple form of the verbs.

When I finished high school, I decided I wanted to
[1] _____ to university and [2] _____
biology. If you're interested in any subject linked to science, it's good to know English well because so many research articles are in English, so I decided to do a course and take an exam.

The day of the exam I was very nervous. I can
[3] _____ lots of information very easily, which is a good thing if you like science and facts, but to
[4] _____ an English exam you need more than information, and I didn't want to [5] _____ it.
I [6] _____ the instructions on the exam paper very carefully, and I [7] _____ all the questions. And then we got to the Speaking task. I became very scared because you do the Speaking task with another student. But then I remembered about all the times we [8] _____ a project and I worked with other students, and I realised it was the same thing. So I relaxed. And I even [9] _____ a very good mark.

Grammar 2 adverbs; writing the correct determiner; open cloze

1 Complete the sentences with the adverb form of these adjectives.

angry	bad	beautiful	careful	early
polite				

1 Caleb shouted _____ at the taxi driver who almost hit him.

2 Meltem was very tired after work, so she went to bed _____ .

3 If you ask _____ , I'll help you.

4 Please check your projects _____ so there are no mistakes.

5 Monica was upset because she did _____ in her exam.

6 Tomas sang _____ during the school concert.

2 Choose the correct answers.

Hi Veronica

Here are the photos I promised you from the
¹ _____ day trip I took with Amy. We went to
Sherwood Forest – you know … Robin Hood's
forest! – because her brother Tim works there as a
guide. We walked through the forest ² _____ and
we saw some ³ _____ birds and animals. We walked
⁴ _____ because we didn't want the animals to be
scared. It's a really great place. You can ⁵ _____
imagine Robin Hood and his Merry Men living
there! And it was a perfect day because the sun
was shining ⁶ _____ . We had a great time. I think I
would like to work there. I'm going to work ⁷ _____
at biology this year, and I'm going to ask Tim how
⁸ _____ it is to get a job looking after the forest.

Talk soon,

Ekaterina

1	**A** amazed	**B** amazing	**C** amazingly
2	**A** slowly	**B** fast	**C** slow
3	**A** beauty	**B** beautiful	**C** beautifully
4	**A** loudly	**B** loud	**C** quietly
5	**A** easily	**B** easy	**C** ease
6	**A** brightly	**B** bright	**C** light
7	**A** good	**B** hardly	**C** hard
8	**A** easily	**B** difficult	**C** close

3 Write sentences with the adverb form of the adjectives in brackets. Use your own ideas.

1 (fast) _____

2 (easy) _____

3 (late) _____

4 (good) _____

5 (happy) _____

6 (careful) _____

4 Read the Exam Reminder and complete the Exam Task.

Exam REMINDER

Writing the correct determiner

- Words that go before nouns, such as *a*, *the*, *some*, *many*, *much*, *my*, *your* and *this*, are called determiners.
- Find the noun. It may be later in the sentence, e.g. after an adjective.
- Is the noun singular or plural, and countable or uncountable?
- Does the noun give new or old information?
- Read the whole text after you finish.

Exam TASK

Open cloze

For each question, write the correct answer. Write **one** word for each gap.

Email Message

From: Salman
To: Ajay

Hi Ajay

How's it going? When we last spoke, you were worried about moving into **(1)** _____ different chemistry class. That's not **(2)** _____ favourite subject, is it? I hope the class isn't too difficult.

I'm joining **(3)** _____ music and drama clubs at my school **(4)** _____ year, which I'm sure will be great fun. I love acting, and I **(5)** _____ already been in some school plays, but not many.

Will you have time to join any clubs? And are you still in the school swimming team?

I have **(6)** _____ go now, but write soon and tell me how things are going.

Salman

⏎ Grammar Reference 9.2, p169 in Student's Book

Writing advantages and disadvantages; planning your time; writing a short essay

Learning REMINDER

Advantages and disadvantages

- Present advantages and disadvantages clearly when you write and don't use the words *advantage* and *disadvantage* too often.
- To present advantages you can use:
  The main advantage of … is that …
  It's also important / useful / good to …
  A good point about … is that ….
- To present disadvantages you can use:
  One disadvantage of … is that …
  Another negative point is …

1 Complete the text with these words.

advantage	disadvantage	negative	positive

1 Should everyone go to university? There are both advantages and disadvantages to this.
2 Some people say that the main ¹ _____ is that you will get a better job if you go to university. You will spend a few years learning your subject, and then people will know that you can work hard and know a lot about your subject. Another ² _____ point is that at university you will meet new people, often from other countries, and learn more than your subject.
3 However, a ³ _____ point is that you will spend not just time but money as well. In many countries, university courses are expensive and students have to borrow money. They worry that they may not earn enough to pay the money back quickly. Another ⁴ _____ may be that while you are at university, your old friends will get jobs, earn money and start new, adult lives before you do. You may lose touch.
4 Although there are some disadvantages, in my opinion it is a good idea to go to university.

2 Read the essay in Exercise 1 again. Match the paragraphs (1–4) with these summaries (a–d).

a Describe the disadvantages. _____
b Introduce the question. _____
c Describe the advantages. _____
d Give your personal opinion. _____

3 Read the essay topic and write the ideas (1–6) in full sentences. Use different phrases to introduce advantages and disadvantages.

Should school students get a weekend job?

1 a way to earn money
_____
_____

2 get some work experience
_____
_____

3 meet interesting people
_____
_____

4 not much free time
_____
_____

5 no time to study
_____
_____

4 Read the Exam Reminder. Why should you plan your time in a writing task?

_____

Exam REMINDER

Planning your time

- For some writing tasks you will have thirty minutes.
- Practise completing the task in that time.
- Plan your time to use it well. For example, allow five minutes for making notes and planning, twenty minutes for writing and five minutes for checking your text.
- Do that for the Exam Task below. Use a timer to check how long you take for each part.

5 Complete the Exam Task. Don't forget to use the Useful Language on page 111 of your Student's Book.

Exam TASK

Writing a short essay

Write an essay to answer the question.

Some people think it is a good idea for students to volunteer in their community. Do you agree? What are the advantages and disadvantages of this idea? Give examples to support your answer.

Reading
finding words with opposite meaning; multiple choice with one text

1 Read the Exam Reminder. Do the words and phrases in the questions always mean the same as words and phrases in the texts?

Exam REMINDER

Finding words with opposite meanings

- In this exam task, some questions check you understood details in a text.
- Words and phrases in the questions may be the opposite of those in the text, but in sentences that mean the same. For example, *It isn't good. = It's bad.*
- Look for questions with words that mean the opposite of those in the text.

2 Now read the text and complete the Exam Task.

Exam TASK

Multiple choice with one text

For each question, choose the correct answer.

1 Harrod dreamed he was a
- **A** guide.
- **B** mechanic.
- **C** photographer.

2 Harrod's funny van photos
- **A** were difficult to take.
- **B** were easy to take.
- **C** were boring to take.

3 People could see Harrod's written message from
- **A** the air.
- **B** the road.
- **C** the side of the van.

4 Where has Harrod been with his van?
- **A** across an ocean
- **B** from New York to California
- **C** to five different countries

5 Harrod's film shows
- **A** the way to build an art car.
- **B** people who build art cars.
- **C** why we need to build more art cars.

The dream machine

One night in 1993, Harrod Blank had a dream about a van, but it was not a normal van – it was covered in cameras. In his dream, he drove around while the van took pictures. People were very surprised and the photos showed that on their faces. When Harrod woke up, he decided to make this dream come true.

He spent two years building this van and he put hundreds of cameras on it. When the van was ready, he travelled around with it, just like in the dream. No one thought the cameras were real. Actually, ten of them worked perfectly. It wasn't difficult for Harrod to take a lot of funny photos.

Harrod used different types of cameras. Some were made in the 1990s, but others were older. He arranged white cameras on top of the car to spell 'Smile', which is what people often say before they take someone's photo. The people along the side of the road, the ones he took pictures of, couldn't see it, but anyone in a plane or helicopter could see it when they flew over the van.

Harrod took his van to a lot of places. His first trip was from California to New York in 1995. In 1998, he took his van by ship to the UK, and he visited five cities in England.

In 2009, Harrod made a film about the idea for his van, *Automorphosis*. In the film, he talks to other people who have made 'art cars' about why they did it and how they feel about it.

Harrod Blank's van

Vocabulary 1 transport (nouns)

1 Write a type of transport under the correct picture.

bike   coach   motorbike   plane   taxi   train

1 _____   2 _____

3 _____   4 _____

5 _____   6 _____

2 What type of transport did these people take? Choose the correct answers.

1 We had an amazing trip across the ocean from Sydney to Hawaii.
   a motorbike   b ship   c coach

2 When we arrived we went straight down on the roof of the building.
   a helicopter   b tram   c plane

3 We got one from the airport. When we arrived at the hotel, I went straight to the reception with our bags while Jim paid the driver.
   a coach   b lorry   c taxi

4 I went with my friend Clare. She's an excellent rider and always carries an extra helmet.
   a tram   b ship   c motorbike

5 There were probably thirty other passengers with us, and it took about twenty-five minutes from the hotel to the city centre. You can get a day ticket.
   a lorry   b taxi   c tram

6 There were some great views of the mountains on the two-day journey from Vancouver to Banff.
   a ship   b train   c tram

7 It was really busy on the roads from London to Birmingham and we arrived two hours late.
   a train   b helicopter   c coach

8 Number 5 goes to the city centre, but sometimes it's full and it drives past my stop.
   a bus   b car   c taxi

3 Complete the conversation with these words.

driving licence   map   passport   petrol
tickets   wheels

Tom: Hey, Liu! When did you get back from Dublin?

Liu: Late last night. We missed our ... what do you call the ships that take your car?

Tom: Ferries?

Liu: Yes, we missed our ferry because Mum left her ¹ _____ at the hotel, so we had to drive back to get it. Luckily, we didn't have to buy ² _____ again.

Tom: But did you have fun in Dublin?

Liu: Oh, yes, But we had some problems there too. One day the police stopped us because one of our ³ _____ was moving in a strange way. They asked to see my father's ⁴ _____ , but he couldn't find it ...

Tom: What happened then?

Liu: He found it, and we called a mechanic who fixed the car. Then we had very little ⁵ _____ , and we arrived at a petrol station just before the car stopped.

Tom: It sounds like you had an adventure there! Was it easy to find your way around?

Liu: Oh, yes, although we didn't have a ⁶ _____ because Mum prefers her phone app, but then one day all our phones lost the internet connection ...

Tom: Ha ha! But what about Dublin?

Liu: I loved it! I want to go back, but not with my parents!

4 Answer the questions with your own ideas.

1 How do you travel to school? Describe what you do from when you close your door to when you arrive at school.
   _____
   _____
   _____ .

2 Do you ever use public transport? Why? / Why not?
   _____
   _____
   _____ .

3 What's the traffic like where you live? Is it safe for children? Give examples to support your opinion.
   _____
   _____
   _____ .

Grammar 1 the passive: present simple

1 **Complete the sentences using the present simple passive form of the verbs.**

1 This new type of bus _____ (drive) by a computer. I think it's scary.

2 Passports _____ (check) when you arrive in a new country.

3 These days, train tickets _____ (often / buy) online.

4 The inside of a train _____ (always / clean) before passengers get on it.

5 Food _____ (not serve) on this train.

6 The bus you're waiting for _____ (usually / delay) because of traffic.

7 Helicopters _____ (not use) for long flights.

8 _____ the fish _____ (cook) in oil?

2 **Rewrite these sentences using the present simple passive.**

1 They close the car park at the station at night.

_____

_____

2 Thousands of people visit the Great Wall of China every year.

_____

_____

3 They send train tickets by email.

_____

_____

4 They sell books and magazines at the airport shop.

_____

_____

5 They usually show bus timetables in the information centre.

_____

_____

6 Passengers turn off their mobile phones during flights.

_____

_____

Listening listening for clues; multiple choice with five conversations

1 **Read the Exam Reminder. When you listen, do you always hear the words in the answer options?**

_____

Exam REMINDER

Listening for clues

- In this exam task there are five conversations on five topics and a question on each.
- Look at each question and option. What will the topic of each conversation be?
- The speakers may not say the words in the answer options. Listen for clues. For example, if the correct answer is *by train*, the speaker may say words like *station*, *ticket office*, etc.

2 **10.1 ▶ Listen and complete the Exam Task.**

Exam TASK

Multiple choice with five conversations

For each question, choose the correct answer.

1 You will hear a man talking to his friend about Rome. Why did he go there?
   A to try the food
   B to see a football match
   C to visit old buildings

2 You will hear two friends talking about visiting a castle. How does Katerina want to go there?
   A by taxi
   B on foot
   C by bus

3 You will hear a woman talking about a trip to Madagascar. What advice does her friend give her?
   A visit the countryside
   B explore the capital
   C go to a small island

4 You will hear two friends talking about a postcard. What's on the postcard?
   A a city centre
   B a bridge
   C a castle

5 You will hear a man talking. Why is he angry?
   A He bought the wrong ticket.
   B His trip was cancelled.
   C The ticket may cost more.

↻ Grammar Reference 10.1, p169 in Student's Book

Vocabulary 2 transport (verbs)

1 **Cross out the words that do not go with the verbs.**

1 get on *a coach/ a car / a bus*
2 take *a taxi / a bike / the tram*
3 ride *a bike / a helicopter / a motorbike*
4 catch *a lorry / a bus / a plane*
5 leave from *the bus station / platform 2 / public transport*
6 miss *a motorbike / a plane / a coach*
7 fly *a ship / a plane / a helicopter*
8 get back *from school / airport / home*
9 pick up *tickets / a helicopter / a friend*
10 cross *the wheel / the river / the road*

2 **Complete the sentences with these verbs.**

catch	drive	fly	get off	miss	park
return	ride	sail	stop		

1 There are no direct buses. We'll need to _____ in the town centre and take the number 7 bus.
2 We had to run to _____ the bus.
3 Do you think it's fun to _____ a motorbike?
4 How long does it take to learn how to _____ a plane?
5 While we were in Greece, we learned how to _____ a boat.
6 Look at the traffic. Do all these people really need to _____ to work?
7 If we _____ our train, we'll have to wait two hours for the next one. So hurry up!
8 There's a place to _____ your bike in front of the museum. You can leave it there and walk straight in.
9 Does the bus _____ outside the train station?
10 We really want to _____ to Krakow soon. It's a lovely city.

3 **Use a dictionary and find the meaning of the words you don't know. Then link each type of transport with the place where you get them.**

1	train	rank	gate
2	coach	harbour	top of the queue
3	flight	railway station	dock
4	taxi	bus station	platform
5	ship	airport	bay

4 **Match the beginning of the sentences (1–8) with the end of the sentences (a–h).**

1 The taxi is on the other side of the street, so we should _____
2 Our stop is the next one, so we need to _____
3 The hotel guests are at the airport, so the driver will _____
4 This place is wonderful. I want to _____
5 Sai is coming by coach, and he will _____
6 I'm afraid I'm lost and I don't know how to _____
7 We don't have time to do any shopping because our plane's going to _____
8 My feet are so tired, and I'll be glad to _____

a pick them up and bring them here.
b arrive at the bus station at 4.00 p.m.
c cross here to get to it.
d get on the train and sit down.
e get back to my hotel.
f leave in thirty minutes.
g get off very soon.
h come back again soon.

5 **Complete the text with the missing verbs.**

Hi Yvonne

How are you? I ^{1} _____ from my holiday yesterday. We had a great time, but I'm really tired from the journey. The train to Florence was ^{2} _____ by two hours, and as a result we ^{3} _____ the train from Florence and all the other trains home. So we ^{4} _____ Florence at 9 p.m. and we didn't ^{5} _____ here until 9 a.m. the next morning. You can ^{6} _____ a bus from the train station to near our home, but yesterday we were too tired for that and we decided to take a taxi. So we ^{7} _____ the street outside the station to where the taxi rank is, ready to queue, but there was only one taxi there and no queue. So we ^{8} _____ it and we didn't have to wait – for the first time in two days!

What about you? How was your holiday?

Speak soon.

Kitty

Grammar 2 the passive: past simple

1 **Complete the sentences using the past simple passive form of these verbs.**

build	complete	delay	film	find
not send	pay for	steal	take	not tell

1 Raj and Nina had an accident and they
_____ to hospital.

2 The oldest bridge in the world _____
more than 2,800 years ago in Turkey.

3 Our new computers _____ by our
school.

4 Where _____ this video
_____ ?

5 The tickets _____ to the correct
address.

6 We're so upset! Both of our bikes
_____ last night!

7 The Shard building in London _____
in 2012.

8 My passport _____ outside the train
station by another passenger.

9 You're an hour late! _____ the train
_____ ?

10 I _____ that I could buy my ticket on
the bus.

2 **Choose the correct answers.**

Barra Airport is in the Outer Hebrides, a group of
islands that are part of Scotland, and it's quite an
unusual airport. It's on a beach which ¹ _____ by the
sea twice a day and when the sea goes down, the
beach ² _____ by planes to bring passengers to the
area. The airport ³ _____ in 1936, and it only flies to
and from one city, Glasgow, the city with the largest
population in Scotland. The flights are short, so food
and drinks ⁴ _____ on the plane. The airport is small,
and it ⁵ _____ by about 10,000 passengers every year.
People love the airport, and it is ⁶ _____ by travellers
as the best airport to visit. Filmmakers love it too, and
many films and TV programmes ⁷ _____ there.

1	A cover	B is covered	C covers
2	A used	B was used	C is used
3	A is opened	B was opened	C were opened
4	A are served	B don't serve	C aren't served
5	A is only visited	B was visited	C only is visited
6	A often chose	B often chosen	C chosen often
7	A was filmed	B is filmed	C are filmed

3 **Write questions for the underlined words using the
past simple passive and the words in brackets.**

1 It was taken <u>at a park in Bangkok</u>. (this photo)
_____
_____

2 It was built <u>in 1492</u>. (this castle)
_____
_____

3 They were chosen <u>because they're Mum's favourite</u>.
(these flowers)
_____
_____

4 It was used <u>for making bread</u>. (this strange thing)
_____
_____

5 They were checked <u>yesterday</u>. (the tests)
_____
_____

6 It was made <u>in Peru</u>. (your handbag)
_____
_____

7 It was parked on the path <u>because the bike park
was full</u>. (the bike)
_____
_____

8 Yes, I was given it for my birthday last year.
(painting of Lake Titicaca)
_____
_____

▶ **Grammar Reference 10.1, p169 in Student's Book**

Writing

conjunctions: *before*, *after* and *while*; adding extra details; writing a story

Learning **REMINDER**

Conjunctions: *before*, *after* and *while*

- Conjunctions make the order of actions clear.
- Look at the timeline, then read the sentences (1–3).

Jin got on the bus.	**7.00**
	7.10 — She started reading her book.
The bus had a problem with the engine.	**7.20**
	7.30 — She texted her dad.
She got off the bus.	**7.40**

1 Jin started reading her book *after* she got on the bus. / *After* Jin got on the bus, she started reading her book.
2 The bus had a problem with the engine *while* she was reading her book. / *While* she was reading her book, the bus had a problem with the engine.
3 She texted her dad *before* she got off the bus. / *Before* she got off the bus, she texted her dad.

1 Connect these sentences using *before*, *after* or *while*.

1 Ben bought a ticket. He got on the train.

_____

2 Soojin sat next to the window on the boat. She got on it.

_____

_____

3 Ali was talking on his phone. The taxi was going up the hill.

_____

_____

4 Dev picked up his things. He got off the bus.

_____

5 Leyla closed all the windows. She left the house.

_____

_____

2 Read the Exam Reminder. What's the advantage of thinking about each character in the story?

Exam **REMINDER**

Adding extra details
- Make sure you understand the story.
- Use the past simple for finished actions.
- Use the past continuous for background events.
- Think about each character in the story: how do they feel? Why do they do what they do?
- Use adjectives to describe the places, the people and their feelings.
- Use conjunctions to connect events and ideas.
- Always read your text carefully.

3 Complete the Exam Task. Don't forget to use the Useful Language on page 123 of your Student's Book.

Exam **TASK**

Writing a story

Look at the three pictures.

Write the story shown in the pictures.

Write **35 words** or more.

Reading
comparing words in the texts and options; multiple choice with six texts

1 Read the Exam Reminder. When answer options have the same words as in the text, are they always the correct answer?

_____

2 Now read the texts and complete the Exam Task.

Exam TASK

Multiple choice with six texts

For each question, choose the correct answer.

1

> **FOR SALE – BICYCLE**
> Adult size. Black with small blue stripes.
> £125 or best offer.
> Call Sven on:
> 01749 765 439

A The bicycle is blue.
B The bicycle may cost less than £125.
C The bicycle is for children.

2

> Hey Annika
> We haven't got any electricity because of the storm. It's a bit dark in the house. Can we study at your place instead?
> Belen

Why did Belen send this text?

A to tell Annika about a storm
B to say it's too dark to see Annika today
C to ask Annika if they can change their plan

3

> WELCOME TO
> **Shenandoah Nature Park**
> • Please stay on walking paths
> • Use bins for rubbish
> • Camping allowed only in some areas

A You can walk anywhere in the park.
B You must leave your rubbish outside the park.
C You must go to a special place for camping.

4

> Hi Rajat
> My flight's delayed. I'm not sure when I'm leaving, but hopefully I'll only have to wait an hour or so. I'll send you a message when I know something.
> Vanya

A Vanya will contact Rajat later.
B Vanya's flight was cancelled.
C Vanya wants Rajat to text her.

5

> SLOW DOWN
> – Bridge closed ahead –
> Icy weather. Please use Hampton Street bridge until further notice.

A There is more information on a notice.
B Cars must drive slowly over the bridge.
C You have to use another way to cross.

6

> Jameel
> Can you please pick your sister up from school today? I can't because I have a meeting at 4.30 p.m. Also, it's going to snow later today, so drive carefully. I'll call you later.
> Mum

A Jameel's mum reminds him to meet her at 4.30 p.m.
B Jameel's mum asks him to do something for her.
C Jameel's mum wants him to call his sister.

Vocabulary 1 weather

1 **Look at the pictures and complete the sentences.**

1 Madrid is having some _____ weather at the moment.

2 There's _____ all over the park. It's so white!

3 It's quite _____ and warm today.

4 It's really _____ right now. I can't see the hills at all!

5 The skies are rather _____ at the moment.

6 There's a lot of _____ today. It isn't a good day for swimming.

2 **Complete the message with these words.**

cloudy	cool	hot	like	rain	storm
sunny	wet				

Hi Levi

We are having a great holiday. It's ¹ _____ here – about 28° C – and it's wonderful to see the sun after all those months of ² _____ weather back at home. Yesterday evening we had dinner outside, at a street market. It was great, although it was a bit ³ _____ and I didn't have my jumper. Two nights ago, there was the most amazing ⁴ _____ and there was a lot of ⁵ _____ . I couldn't sleep because of the noise on the roof! The next morning it was bright and ⁶ _____ again, so we went to the beach. What's the weather ⁷ _____ there? Has it stopped raining? Are you and Nadar going camping this weekend or is it going to be too ⁸ _____ ?

See you soon

Yanisa

3 **Complete the conversation with weather words. More than one answer may be possible.**

A: Hey! Come and see. Here's the weather forecast.

B: Wow! What should we pack? High temperatures at the weekend … look: 39°C during the day, with sunshine.

A: That's ¹ _____ ! But look at the night temperatures: 5°C. That will feel really ² _____ , especially after the day temperatures.

B: That's not too bad – it's better for sleeping. But look at the wind: 30 kilometres per hour!

A: Ah, that's ³ _____ – let's hope the tent stays down! But it'll only be like that on Sunday, and then it'll be OK.

B: True, but then the rain will come …

A: Yes, it looks like a ⁴ _____ Monday with no sunshine, but Tuesday will be the worst – heavy rain all day … It'll be very ⁵ _____ ! Wait – is that snow on Thursday?

B: I'm sure that will be high up in the mountains. The lowest temperature we'll have is 5°C, which is too ⁶ _____ for snow. But rain in high temperatures may mean it'll be ⁷ _____ when the rain stops, so we won't be able to see far.

A: Maybe we should wait and go away a different week.

Grammar 1 comparatives

1 **Complete the sentences with the correct comparative form of the adjectives and adverbs.**

1 Today's maths test was a lot _____ (hard) the one last week.

2 It's very windy today, and the wind is much _____ (strong) it was yesterday.

3 Is too much rain _____ (good) no rain at all?

4 My computer doesn't work _____ (fast) as it used to.

5 We drove _____ (far) on our American trip _____ we drove on our European one.

6 Icy roads are always _____ (dangerous) wet ones.

7 I'm not a very good driver, but my brother Hal drives _____ (badly) I do.

8 The weather this afternoon is not as _____ (cold) it was this morning.

2 **The words in bold are incorrect. Write the correct form.**

San Francisco has quite unusual weather. It's not as ¹ **warmer** as some people might think, even in the summer. It's in California, but it's on the Pacific Ocean and it's ² **cold** than the city of Los Angeles to the south. There is also a lot of fog. It comes from the ocean, so it is ³ **foggy** than many other places in California. It's amazing to see the fog over the city. Some people there want it to be ⁴ **sunny** than it usually is. There is often so much fog that it covers the sun, though the fog moves more ⁵ **quicker** than normal clouds do. It also rains more ⁶ **heavy** there than places in the south, so if you're looking for some hot weather, go south!

1 _____   4 _____

2 _____   5 _____

3 _____   6 _____

3 **Write sentences comparing the weather where you are with the weather in San Francisco.**

1 _____

_____

_____

2 _____

_____

3 _____

_____

_____

Listening
listening for negative verbs; multiple choice with picture options

1 **Read the Exam Reminder. If a speaker says they almost didn't do something, did they do it or not?**

_____

Exam REMINDER

Listening for negative verbs

- Sometimes speakers use words like *almost*, *nearly* or *until* + a negative verb to say that something happened or will happen. For example: *I nearly didn't go* = *I nearly decided not to go, but then I went. We're not eating until 8 p.m.* = *We're eating at 8 p.m. or after.*
- Listen carefully when you hear a negative verb used with *almost*, *nearly* or *until*.

2 **11.1** ▶ **Listen and complete the Exam Task.**

Exam TASK

Multiple choice with picture options

For each question, choose the correct answer.

1 What did Billy do yesterday?

A   B   C

2 How much did Javier pay for his jumper?

£20	£40	£70
A	B	C

3 When is Clara's train leaving?

A   B   C

4 What's the weather like in Lucia's town?

A   B   C

5 When is Paolo going on holiday?

A   B   C

▶ Grammar Reference 11.1, p169 in Student's Book

Vocabulary 2
extreme weather; weather collocations; recognising common phrasal verbs; multiple-choice cloze

1 Write the extreme weather that these people are talking about.

| drought | hurricane | thunder | wildfire |

1 'We got the news two days before it arrived. We put wood on the windows, and we drove to my grandparents' house. It rained for three days and a lot of trees fell down because of the strong winds. Then we returned home and I'm happy to say that our house was still there.' _____

2 'It was late at night and I was sleeping. Suddenly I heard it. It was so loud. I almost jumped out of bed! It started raining a few minutes later. It was just a quick storm, but it was above the house and the noise I heard … wow!' _____

3 'I saw it in the forest at the top of the mountain. I was really afraid. We left the house to go to my aunt and uncle's place across town. We waited for a few hours, and then we heard that it was out. Luckily, our home was OK and everybody was safe, but there's no forest now. What a disaster!'

_____

4 'We planted lots of vegetables in the spring, but it was a really bad summer and by August, everything was dead. Some of the trees also looked quite unhealthy as the leaves were brown. It didn't rain until September. I hope we don't have another summer like that again.' _____

2 Cross out the word that does NOT fit with the noun after it.

1 Paris was covered in *light / soft / strong* snow.

2 A hurricane usually brings very *heavy / high / strong* winds.

3 It may be better to stay inside when there are very *low / high / weak* temperatures.

4 I can see *dark / deep / white* clouds today.

5 Umbrellas are useful in *heavy / high / light* rain.

3 Complete the sentences with adjectives from Exercise 2.

1 There are often _____ temperatures here, so you should bring warm clothes.

2 Look at those _____ clouds. It's going to rain soon.

3 It's just some _____ rain – I won't get very wet.

4 Put a hat on today – the sun is very _____ .

5 We can go sailing. There will only be _____ winds.

6 If you drive on snow, it won't be _____ or soft any more.

4 Read the Exam Reminder and complete the Exam Task.

Exam TASK

Multiple-choice cloze
For each question, choose the correct answer.

Which place in the world gets the most rain? Mawsynram is the correct answer. Mawsynram is a village in eastern India, very **(1)** _____ to Bangladesh, with a population of 1,300. It gets 1,187.1 centimetres of rain every year. For that reason, the area around it has a lot of **(2)** _____ . Mawsynram is between high **(3)** _____ and low fields. In the rainy season, very warm wet air **(4)** _____ to the north. It hits the hills behind Mawsynram and it turns into rain. And the rainy season **(5)** _____ usually nine months long. That's why people always **(6)** _____ on a raincoat and take an umbrella when they go out.

1	A closely	B closed	C close
2	A waters	B rivers	C seas
3	A islands	B lakes	C hills
4	A travels	B changes	C leaves
5	A has	B is	C takes
6	A put	B get	C try

Grammar 2 superlatives; writing the correct grammar words; open cloze

1 Complete the sentences with the superlative form of these adjectives.

| beautiful | bright | cold | frightening |
| sunny | wet | | |

1 Put on some warm clothes! It will be _____ day of the week today.

2 That storm last night was awful. It was _____ storm all year!

3 In Greece it rains a lot in December. It's _____ month of the year.

4 There are many bright stars in the night sky, but Sirius is _____.

5 Many areas of Europe are pretty in the spring, but I think the Spanish countryside is _____.

6 Yuma, in the US, gets over four thousand hours of sun in a year. It's _____ place on Earth.

2 Complete the sentences with a superlative adverb.

1 Sonia was in third place in the race, Monica came second, and Rhea came first. Rhea ran _____.

2 On 22nd June, the sun is very high in the sky. On this day, the sun shines _____.

3 India gets most of its rain in the summer. During this time of the year, it rains _____.

4 Jack arrived at the party at 9 p.m., Ferdinand arrived at 9.30 p.m. and Gus arrived at 10 p.m. Gus arrived _____.

5 Out of all the people I know, Fredricka swims _____. She is always the last to finish.

6 On Mount Everest, the wind blows _____ between November and February.

3 Complete the sentences with the superlative form of the adjective or adverb and your own ideas.

1 The _____ (funny) person I know is _____.

2 The _____ (beautiful) city in my country is _____.

3 The _____ (sun) month in my country is _____.

4 The person I know who works _____ (hard) is _____.

5 Where I live the rain falls _____ (heavily) in _____.

4 Read the Exam Reminder and complete the Exam Task.

Exam TASK

Open cloze

For each question, write the correct answer.

Write **one** word for each gap.

Hi Ali

How are you?

Here's some more news about my holiday **(1)** _____ New Zealand. Today we're in Wellington, which my guidebook says is **(2)** _____ windiest city in the world. I didn't know that, but I can tell you that it's windier **(3)** _____ any other place I've ever been. That explains why so many people **(4)** _____ surfing in the ocean – windsurfing seems very popular too. I've never tried that, but I'm sure riding the waves is a great feeling. And it's the **(5)** _____ amazing sport to watch.

How are things in Riyadh? We're getting **(6)** _____ on 22nd July, so I'll see you then.

Bye for now,

Nasser

▶ Grammar Reference 11.2, p170 in Student's Book

Writing
describing a trip; using different tenses; ordering events and adding interest; writing an article

1 Write sentences with these words. Use the present simple, past simple or present continuous.

1 Tokyo / be / the capital of Japan

_____

2 I / go / Egyptian Museum in Cairo yesterday

_____

3 Next summer / we / visit / Lisbon

_____

4 Last night / we / watch / a great film on TV

_____

5 Later today / we / go / to the beach

_____

_____

2 Complete this student's essay with the correct form of these verbs.

be	have got	hear	learn	stay
take	travel	visit	walk	

Last summer, I ¹ _____ Scotland. Our first stop was Edinburgh, which is the capital.

On the first day, we ² _____ a guided tour around the city centre. I ³ _____ a lot about the history of the city. It ⁴ _____ a wonderful castle, which you can see from anywhere in the city, and the next day we went inside it. We ⁵ _____ around for hours and ⁶ _____ stories of kings and queens. What an amazing building!

On the third day we left Edinburgh and ⁷ _____ to Loch Ness, which ⁸ _____ a lake in the north of Scotland. It was a great trip.

This summer, we ⁹ _____ in York, in the north of England. I've seen photos of its old streets, and I'm really looking forward to visiting it.

3 Read the Exam Reminder. Why should you include details in your article?

_____

Exam REMINDER

Ordering events and adding interest
- Some writing tasks may ask you to write an article about an event. You can write about a true event or imagine one.
- Describe events in the order they happened.
- Use time expressions to make the order clear.
- Use conjunctions to connect events and ideas logically.
- Use adjectives to describe the places, the people and your feelings.
- Think about the reader. Include facts or details that will interest them.
- Finish your article with your opinion.

4 Complete the Exam Task. Don't forget to use the Useful Language on page 135 of your Student's Book.

Exam TASK

Writing an article
Imagine that you and some friends are from another country and you went on a trip to your city or town. Write an article (70–100 words) for your online blog. You should:

- describe where you went and say why it was interesting
- say what you did while you were there
- give your opinion about the trip and talk about another place to visit

You should plan your article before you begin writing. Think about what you are going to write and make some notes to help you in this box:

Now write your article of 70–100 words.

Reading
answers summarising parts of a text; multiple choice with one text

1 **Read the Exam Reminder. How do you choose the right answer option when it is a summary?**

a look for specific details in the text

b think of the overall meaning of sentences in the text

c find the same words in the text

2 **Now read the text and complete the Exam Task.**

Cycle, recycle and upcycle

In the late 1990s, some people in Edinburgh in Scotland had an idea. Their children went to Sciennes Primary School, and the parents started a clever way to reuse their children's good bikes: when a child's bike became too small for them, their parents gave it to another family with a smaller child and they got a bike from a family with an older child who was too tall for it. So all the children had a good bike that was the right size for them and the parents didn't need to keep buying new bikes.

The idea became very popular, and more and more people started giving and taking bikes. However, this created another problem: often a bike was given, but it wasn't taken until a week later or longer, and some parents' gardens were full of bikes. They decided they couldn't do this from their homes any more.

Vocabulary 1 places in the countryside; points of the compass

1 Look at the map and complete the sentences with *north*, *south*, *east* or *west*.

1 Cardiff is _____ of London.
2 Inverness is _____ of Edinburgh.
3 Birmingham is _____ of Manchester.
4 Glasgow is _____ of Edinburgh.
5 Cambridge is _____ of London.
6 London is _____ of Oxford.

That's how a new organisation was born: first they moved into a small building in the city, then the parents opened a shop in Edinburgh's Waverley train station and they called it The Bike Station. People of all ages started to use it, so they had to move to an even bigger place. Now people give them old bikes and the Bike Station fixes them, recycles them, upcycles them – that is, they make them better than when they were new – and sells them at good prices. Today they have shops in Glasgow and Perth too, and the Bike Station is now the largest bicycle recycling organisation in Scotland.

Their purpose is to encourage people to use bikes as a form of transport. They organise classes to teach people how to fix their bikes. They even organise free social rides for people who are a bit scared to ride in the city streets: they start in a quiet area, then go where there's a bit more traffic and then to the city centre – so people make new friends, keep fit and protect the environment.

2 Complete the sentences with these words.

desert	forest	lake	mountain	river	sea

1 How many days does it take to sail across the _____?
2 Birds, insects and many different types of large animals make their home in a _____.
3 The _____ is very hot in the day and very cold at night.
4 There is a small _____ that goes through the park, and you have to use the bridge to cross it.
5 What is the highest _____ in your country?
6 There is a very beautiful _____ near the campsite that is perfect for swimming.

3 Which places are these speakers talking about? Choose the correct answer.

1 **A:** This looks like a good place to swim.
   B: Wow, the water is really clean.
   a hill **b** field **c** beach

2 **A:** Let's walk along here by the river.
   B: Good idea. I'd like to see where it goes.
   a beach **b** path **c** island

3 **A:** Have you ever explored this forest, Liam?
   B: Well, it's not really a forest – it's not that big!
   a field **b** beach **c** wood

4 **A:** Are those tomato plants? There are lots of them!
   B: They look really good. Let's go and ask the farmer if he can sell us some.
   a wood **b** hill **c** field

5 **A:** It takes a long time to climb up here, but you can see almost as far as the sea.
   B: I know. What a beautiful view!
   a hill **b** field **c** beach

6 **A:** It's not very big, is it?
   B: You're right. You can probably sail around it in a few hours.
   a island **b** path **c** hill

Grammar 1 ordering adjectives

1 Write the adjective categories in the correct order.

age	colour	material	nationality
opinion	shape	size	

1   2   3   4   5   6   7

opinion

2 Choose the correct words to complete the sentences. Remember the rules of the order of adjectives.

1 She's got a large *lovely / rectangular* table in her living room.

2 Benjamin's got medium-sized *comfortable / old* chairs in his living room.

3 Is that your new *big / red* car in front of the school?

4 These items go in the *plastic / small* blue bin.

5 She's wearing a *comfortable / cotton* old T-shirt.

6 Juan keeps some small things from his trip to Cuba in a round *metal / strange* box.

7 We went to the new *Italian / fantastic* restaurant last night.

8 Did you see the beautiful *horrible / silk* dress Jess was wearing?

3 Complete the sentences with the adjectives. Use them in the correct order.

1 They are building a _____ garden in our park. (pretty / Japanese / small)

2 She put the _____ box in the recycling bin. (square / ugly / wooden)

3 They sell _____ biscuits at the market. (little / English / delicious)

4 Giuseppe lives in a _____ house. (new / lovely / green)

5 This museum has got _____ vases. (Greek / old / beautiful)

6 Can you give me that _____ plate over there? (white / plastic / round)

Listening listening to how speakers respond; multiple choice with one conversation

1 Read the Exam Reminder. Do people always give positive answers by saying *yes*?

2 **12.1▶** Listen and complete the Exam Task.

Exam TASK

Multiple choice with one conversation

For each question, choose the correct answer.

You will hear Myra talking to her friend, Paul, about a holiday.

1 Who is Paul going on holiday with?
  A his parents
  B a friend of the family
  C his sister

2 The island is
  A south of Italy.
  B east of Sardinia.
  C west of Corsica.

3 Paul says that
  A there aren't many tuna fish in the sea now.
  B tuna fish are very dangerous.
  C the beaches are safe.

4 What does Paul want to do?
  A go biking in the countryside
  B eat ice-cream on the beach
  C meet new people in the village

5 Paul is going to take photos with his
  A digital camera.
  B mobile phone.
  C tablet.

↻ **Grammar Reference 12.1, p170 in Student's Book**

Vocabulary 2 animals; the environment

1 Complete the sentences with these words.

| bear | bee | butterfly | dolphin | duck |
| mouse | shark | snake | | |

1 Be careful! There's a _____ flying above your head.

2 We saw a big brown _____ on our camping trip. Luckily it didn't run towards us.

3 There was a brown and white _____ in the park. That's a long way from the lake!

4 It looks like a small animal has eaten your bread – you may have a _____ in your home!

5 I saw a purple _____ in the garden today. It was resting on one of the flowers.

6 It is not safe to swim here. Someone saw a _____ in the water the other day.

7 A _____ swam very near our boat, and then lots followed it. They looked very friendly.

8 My brother saw a green _____ in the forest. He got away from it quickly, because he didn't know if it was dangerous.

2 Write a category for each of these animals – *bird, fish, insect, mammal* or *reptile*.

1 bear _____

2 bee _____

3 butterfly _____

4 dolphin _____

5 duck _____

6 mouse _____

7 shark _____

8 snake _____

3 Write descriptions for the animals.

1 A bear _____
_____
_____
_____ .

2 A bee _____
_____
_____
_____ .

3 A dolphin _____
_____
_____
_____ .

4 A shark _____
_____
_____
_____ .

4 Choose the correct answers.

For a class project, we are [1] ___ vegetables in a garden. My mum and dad helped me with it and here's what we did:

We [2] ___ some seeds in the garden and we [3] ___ after them every day. We gave them [4] ___ a few times during the week, and soon we began to see little green plants. After a few weeks, they turned into lovely plants with small flowers. We started to see some insects in the garden. We saw colourful [5] ___, and they were beautiful. I wanted to see some birds in the garden too, so my dad and I [6] ___ a bird feeder. My mum gave me some nuts to [7] ___ it with. At some point, we started to see a few [8] ___. They are good for a garden, but I didn't get near them.

After about three months, we had some fresh vegetables. I even got some new seeds from them. I will [9] ___ them and use them later for new plants. I'm going to talk about my project in class and I'll take my favourite vegetable to show everyone – a bright red tomato.

1	A using	B growing	C filling
2	A planted	B made	C used
3	A saw	B looked	C watched
4	A electricity	B water	C food
5	A butterflies	B snakes	C mice
6	A grew	B saved	C made
7	A put	B fill	C save
8	A sharks	B ducks	C bees
9	A save	B fill	C plant

Grammar 2 adjectives ending -ing and -ed

1 Look at the verbs. Complete the conversations with the correct form of the adjectives for each verb.

TIRE

1 **A:** Camping in the forest was fun, but it was also _____.

B: Were you very _____ when you got home?

BORE

2 **A:** I get _____ when I watch documentaries.

B: Maybe you've only watched _____ ones.

AMAZE

3 **A:** The trip to the nature park was really _____.

B: You look _____ in all the photos!

INTEREST

4 **A:** I'm really _____ in dolphins.

B: I watched a really _____ programme about them last night. Did you watch it too?

FRIGHTEN

5 **A:** Dilek saw a rather _____ spider in the garden.

B: That's why she looked so _____ when she came in!

EXCITE

6 **A:** Your trip to the rainforest sounds very _____.

B: I know! I'm very _____ about going there!

2 Choose the correct words to complete the sentences.

1 The children were very *excited / exciting* to hold a baby bear.

2 It was really *amused / amusing* when the monkey took somebody's drink!

3 I was really *frightened / frightening* when I saw the snake in the forest.

4 The programme about reptiles was *fascinated / fascinating*.

5 Rainforests are *amazed / amazing* – so many different kinds of wildlife live in them.

6 I got a great mark in my test. It was really *surprised / surprising*.

7 My dad wasn't *amused / amusing* by my joke.

8 Do you understand this film? I'm really *confused / confusing* by the story.

3 Complete the text with the correct form of the verbs.

Antarctica is a beautiful place, but some people may find it a bit [1] _____ (frighten), especially in the summer, when you never see the sun. From the end of March until September, you can only see the moon and the stars. So, for six months, there's very little natural light. Many [2] _____ (interest) people visit Antarctica because they want to learn more about it. However, they don't go until it's autumn because it's too dark during the other times of the year.

Travelling around Antarctica is very [3] _____ (tire). There aren't many roads and they are usually covered in snow. The area is very difficult to explore, but visitors say Antarctica is an [4] _____ (amaze) place that's full of great adventure. The bright white snow and deep blue ocean are [5] _____ (excite) to see. Of course, there are no cities in Antarctica. If you like life in the city, you might become a bit [6] _____ (bore).

4 Complete the sentences with your own ideas.

1 I'm really interested in _____.

2 I'm very frightened of _____.

3 I was bored when _____.

4 I was excited when _____.

5 I think _____ is amazing.

6 _____ is really exciting.

7 _____ is boring because _____.

8 _____ was really interesting.

9 _____ are more frightening than _____.

10 _____ is more tiring than _____.

> ⟳ Grammar Reference 12.2, p170 in Student's Book

Writing
helping the environment; structuring an essay; organising your ideas; writing a short essay

1 Read the Learning Reminder and the essay question. Then read the sentences (A–E) and decide which paragraph they should go in: 1, 2 or 3.

Some beaches in tourist areas are quite dirty. Tourists leave rubbish on the beach, and a beautiful place starts to look rather ugly. What can we do to get tourists to keep beaches clean? Give examples in your answer.

A One way to help is to put up signs. Signs can tell people not to leave their rubbish. ___

B Another way to help is to place rubbish bins in many areas of the beach. ___

C I am sure that by using signs, placing bins and talking to tourists, we can make a difference. ___

D Many tourists visit beaches because they are beautiful. However, they leave rubbish there, and the area looks very dirty. ___

E A third way to help is by telling tourists to keep the beach clean. For example, if someone throws rubbish on the beach, you should ask them politely to use a bin. ___

2 Choose the correct answers.

1 A lot of pollution in our cities _____ cars and the petrol they use.
   a causes   **b** is caused by   **c** caused

2 Bikes are a great way to use less petrol. _____ bikes don't need petrol to work.
   a One way is   **b** This is because   **c** However,

3 One way to help is by riding a bike. _____, people who live close to their office should use a bike to get to work.
   a For example,   **b** Another way   **c** However,

4 Buses use petrol, but they are better than cars. _____ they can carry many people at once.
   a However,   **b** For example,   **c** This is because

5 Sometimes we have to travel by car. _____, we don't have to drive one that uses a lot of petrol.
   a This is because   **b** However,   **c** For example,

3 Read the exam question and complete the notes with the headings in the box.

People use cars to go to work and go shopping. However, a lot of pollution is caused by cars and the petrol they use. What can we do to use less petrol every day? Give examples to support your answer.

| Drive a car that uses less petrol   Ride a bike |
| Use public transport more often |

Ways to use less petrol:

1
  - buses use petrol, but are better than cars
  - can carry many people at once

2
  - if live close to office, should ride to work
  - can ride to shops near home and leave car

3
  - may need to drive, but can use less petrol
  - think about the one you choose

4 Read the Exam Reminder. Why should you do before you turn your notes into an essay?

_____

5 Complete the Exam Task. Write your plan first.

Exam TASK

Writing a short essay

What can young people do to teach adults to look after our planet? Give examples to support your answer.

Vocabulary

1 Choose the correct answer.

1 I have two _____ . They are my mum's sister's children.
   a sisters
   b aunts
   c cousins
   d uncles

2 Johanna and Rasmus have a boy and a girl. Their _____ 's name is Karl and he's five.
   a son
   b mother
   c uncle
   d brother

3 A: This person writes that her date of birth is 02/04/05, and she's American.
   B: Her birthday is in _____ .
   a January
   b February
   c March
   d April

4 Danielle is French. Her sister was born in _____ too. Paris, I think.
   a France
   b England
   c the UK
   d Spain

5 Your mum's son is your _____ .
   a brother
   b father
   c sister
   d son

6 A: Who is that man?
   B: That's Erica's _____ , Juan Carlos. They are married and have a daughter.
   a grandfather
   b brother
   c husband
   d father

7 Your dad's sister is your _____ .
   a mum
   b sister
   c uncle
   d aunt

8 A: This man writes that his date of birth is 09/11/03. Is his birthday in September?
   B: No, he's British. His birthday's in _____ .
   a March
   b August
   c October
   d November

9 I have four _____ – my dad's parents and my mum's parents.
   a nieces
   b uncles
   c grandparents
   d parents

10 That's Maria. She and Jorge are married. She is Jorge's _____ .
   a wife
   b sister
   c mother
   d daughter

Grammar

2 Choose the correct answer.

1 My penpals Omar and Karim _____ in Cairo.
   a is living
   b living
   c live
   d lives

2 A: When do you do your homework?
   B: I _____ it in the evenings after dinner.
   a do usually
   b usually
   c does usually
   d usually do

3 A: _____ exactly do you live in Morocco?
   B: I live in Rabat.
   a Who
   b Where
   c When
   d What

4 Why _____ forget to bring your dictionary to school?
   a you always
   b do always
   c do you always
   d you do always

5 Kadir _____ late for football training.
   a be never
   b is never
   c never is
   d never be

6 Aisyah and Najwa _____ that song again! I think it is the hundredth time today!
   a plays
   b 's playing
   c play
   d are playing

7 I _____ a YouTube video right now.
   a 'm not watching
   b don't watch
   c 'm watching not
   d not watch

8 What book _____ at the moment?
   a you read
   b you're reading
   c do you read
   d are you reading

9 I'm a bit shy and I _____ in class. Only when we work in pairs.
   a not often talk
   b not talking often
   c don't often talk
   d 'm not often talking

10 A: Alejandro is quite a good student.
   B: I agree. He _____ an exam.
   a 's hardly ever failing
   b hardly ever fails
   c hardly fails ever
   d fails hardly ever

Vocabulary

1 Choose the correct answer.

1 **A:** I really like your _____ socks, Gaelle.
  B: Thanks! Blue and green are my favourite colours.
  a white   **c** stripy
  b silver   **d** red

2 My feet really hurt. I hate these new _____ !
  a boots   **c** skirts
  b hats   **d** belts

3 It's cold, so you need to wear a _____ to stay warm.
  a skirt   **c** jacket
  b tie   **d** belt

4 **A:** What clothes are good to wear to a wedding?
  B: Formal clothes like a _____ .
  a jumper   **c** handbag
  b suit   **d** necklace

5 It's important to wear a good pair of _____ when you are exercising.
  a belts   **c** trainers
  b shirts   **d** trousers

6 Monica is very _____ . She got all the answers right in the history test.
  a friendly   **c** clever
  b lovely   **d** beautiful

7 My cousin's so _____ . She talks all the time!
  a noisy   **c** careful
  b tired   **d** heavy

8 The maths lesson yesterday was really _____ .
  a tired   **c** bored
  b busy   **d** boring

9 The book looked _____ , so I bought it.
  a interesting   **c** interested
  b boring   **d** tiring

10 **A:** Eliot's quite a _____ person.
   B: I know, he's always telling great jokes.
   a kind   **c** funny
   b noisy   **d** quiet

Grammar

2 Choose the correct answer.

1 Palestina _____ a swimming costume when she jumped into the water.
  a wore   **c** wears
  b was wearing   **d** used to wear

2 They _____ for Natalia for over an hour and then they left.
  a wait   **c** waits
  b was waiting   **d** waited

3 My sister _____ have long hair. Now she has short hair.
  a was   **c** use to
  b didn't use   **d** used to

4 Where _____ to live before they moved here?
  a do they use   **c** did they use
  b they used   **d** they used to

5 _____ to play football when you were young?
  a You used   **c** Did you use
  b You used to   **d** Do you use

6 I _____ to the bus stop when the bus suddenly left.
  a am walking   **c** was walking
  b walk   **d** walked

7 This morning it _____ , so I stayed at home and did my homework.
  a were raining   **c** rained
  b raining   **d** was raining

8 Dad was clearing the table while I _____ the washing up.
  a were doing   **c** was doing
  b does   **d** do

9 **A:** _____ dinner when I called yesterday?
  B: Yes, but I was happy to hear from you.
  a You were having **c** Did you have
  b You had   **d** Were you having

10 I was thinking about the Carnival when the teacher _____ me a question.
   a asked   **c** were asking
   b asks   **d** was asking

Vocabulary

1 Choose the correct answer.

1 I can't read the text on the _____ of your phone.
  a screen   **c** camera
  b tablet   **d** printer

2 A: Is Julie going to the party on Saturday?
  B: I'm not sure, but I can _____ her to find out.
  a go   **c** text
  b check   **d** send

3 A: Did you do anything last night?
  B: I _____ a cool video from the internet and watched it.
  a sent   **c** made
  b chatted   **d** downloaded

4 I took my _____ in the garden to do my homework.
  a digital camera **c** laptop
  b printer   **d** screen

5 A: How's your friend in Cameroon?
  B: I'm not sure. I sent him a(n) _____ . I hope to hear from him soon.
  a internet   **c** email
  b web   **d** password

6 My mum's computer is really _____ , so it's very slow.
  a modern   **c** normal
  b old   **d** easy

7 A: This morning we're learning about the history of the computer.
  B: Oh, we're learning about _____ thing then, but our lesson is this afternoon.
  a an unusual   **c** a different
  b a terrible   **d** the same

8 A: Do you think maths is _____ ?
  B: No, not at all. I really enjoy it.
  a easy   **c** boring
  b normal   **d** interesting

9 That's a very _____ camera. You wear it on your head.
  a unusual   **c** difficult
  b normal   **d** excellent

10 How much time do you usually spend on _____ media?
  a mobile   **c** social
  b online   **d** digital

Grammar

2 Choose the correct answer.

1 I _____ a train to Johannesburg this afternoon.
  a take   **c** 'm taking
  b taking   **d** takes

2 Where _____ on holiday this year?
  a you're going   **c** are you going
  b you go   **d** do you go

3 A: What are your plans for tomorrow?
  B: We _____ Oscar and Emilia in the park.
  a 's meeting   **c** meet
  b meets   **d** 're meeting

4 _____ at the concert hall this week?
  a Are they playing **c** They play
  b Playing   **d** They are playing

5 A: What happened to your skiing plans?
  B: I changed my mind. I _____ .
  a 'm going   **c** don't go
  b go   **d** 'm not going

6 Do you often eat dinner late _____ night?
  a on   **c** in
  b to   **d** at

7 A: Where does Ricardo live?
  B: He lives _____ New York.
  a for   **c** on
  b in   **d** at

8 They changed the day of the English exam. It's _____ Wednesday now.
  a in   **c** at
  b of   **d** on

9 We're not going to Egypt next week. We're going _____ July.
  a on   **c** to
  b in   **d** at

10 Maja walked _____ the library, sat down and started studying.
  a from   **c** into
  b toward   **d** to

Vocabulary

1 **Choose the correct answer.**

1 _____ are a carbohydrate that many people eat.
  a Oranges   **c** Onions
  b Eggs   **d** Potatoes

2 **A:** Are you going to put _____ on the pizza?
  B: Of course!
  a lemons   **c** milk
  b mushrooms   **d** butter

3 I don't drink _____ because I don't like the taste of it.
  a rice   **c** milk
  b fish   **d** meat

4 Do you eat a lot of _____ , like bananas and oranges?
  a meat   **c** fruit
  b cereal   **d** vegetables

5 Chickens give us fresh _____ .
  a tomatoes   **c** cheese
  b grapes   **d** eggs

6 _____ the oven to 175° C before you put the cake in it.
  a Pre-heat   **c** Bake
  b Mix   **d** Cook

7 **A:** How much butter do we need for this recipe?
  B: I think it's 300 _____ .
  a kilos   **c** degrees
  b grams   **d** centimetres

8 _____ all the ingredients together with a spoon.
  a Cut   **c** Add
  b Roll   **d** Mix

9 **A:** How big do you cut each piece of dough?
  B: They need to be about eight _____ long.
  a degrees   **c** metres
  b centimetres   **d** kilometres

10 **A:** What do we do with the biscuit dough when we finish mixing it?
  B: We _____ it out.
  a roll   **c** mix
  b bake   **d** add

Grammar

2 **Choose the correct answer.**

1 **A:** Which recipe did you decide to use?
  B: I _____ use a new recipe. I found it on the internet.
  a 'm going   **c** going to
  b 'm going to   **d** will

2 **A:** Karl, this food is really cold!
  B: OK. I _____ it in the oven for a few minutes.
  a 'm going to put   **c** going to put
  b 'll put   **d** put

3 I think I _____ the pizza for our lunch now.
  a going to order   **c** 'll order
  b 'm going to order   **d** order

4 **A:** Do you need snacks for the party tomorrow?
  B: No, Steve _____ something to eat.
  a 's going to prepare   **c** will prepare
  b going to prepare   **d** prepares

5 **A:** It's very hot today. I'm really thirsty.
  B: _____ get you a glass of water.
  a I'll   **c** I'm going to
  b I   **d** I'm going

6 We need _____ peppers to make this meal.
  a any   **c** some
  b few   **d** an

7 _____ there any news from the cake shop? What time is the cake going to be ready?
  a Are   **c** Will
  b Is going to be   **d** Is

8 **A:** Do you want milk in your coffee?
  B: No, but I'd like a _____ sugar in it, please.
  a much   **c** few
  b little   **d** some

9 **A:** How _____ food does a lion eat every day?
  B: Probably a lot!
  a few   **c** many
  b some   **d** much

10 There are _____ of mangoes on this tree. They're delicious!
  a many   **c** little
  b much   **d** lots

Vocabulary

1 Choose the correct answer.

1 My room is just down the _____ and to the right.
a hall
b garden
c garage
d window

2 A: Where are we having lunch?
B: In the _____ .
a stairs
b dining room
c ceiling
d roof

3 Can you close the _____ to my room, please?
a stairs
b hall
c door
d wall

4 Dad and I planted a big tree in the _____ last weekend.
a kitchen
b garden
c bedroom
d bathroom

5 This _____ is not clean – I can't see my face clearly.
a carpet
b lamp
c painting
d mirror

6 Mum parked the car in the _____ , went into the house and sat down.
a garage
b hall
c roof
d bathroom

7 I can hear the rain falling on the _____ of our house.
a garden
b wall
c roof
d hall

8 A: This is a really comfortable _____ .
B: Yes, and four people can sit on it.
a armchair
b sofa
c shelf
d bookcase

9 Can you open the _____ on that window? It's dark in here.
a bath
b shower
c carpet
d curtains

10 A: Mum, what's wrong with the _____ ?
B: There's a problem with it. You can have a bath in the other bathroom.
a towel
b toilet
c shower
d lamp

Grammar

2 Choose the correct answer.

1 A: Dana lives on a really cool houseboat.
B: Yes, I _____ it before.
a was seeing
b have seen
c saw
d see

2 They _____ a new house across the street.
a 've built just
b built just
c 've just built
d just have built

3 We've lived here _____ 2017.
a yet
b already
c since
d for

4 _____ the living room yet?
a Did you clean
b You have cleaned
c Are you cleaning
d Have you cleaned

5 A: Why is Oliver worried?
B: He _____ house before.
a never moved
b 's never moved
c never has moved
d 's moved

6 A: Where do these games go?
B: They go in the _____ bedrooms.
a boys
b boy
c boy's
d boys'

7 _____ notebook is the one with a picture of a pink sofa on it.
a Jess'
b Jesss'
c Jesses
d Jess

8 A: Is this Stephanie's book?
B: Yes, that's _____ . She had it with her in the classroom.
a she
b yours
c her
d hers

9 A: Which house belongs to Rafaella and Ricardo?
B: _____ house is number three.
a His
b Her
c Theirs
d Their

10 A: This is my tablet, Leo.
B: No, it's _____ . Dad said we had to share it.
a mine
b theirs
c ours
d his

Vocabulary

1 **Choose the correct answer.**

1 Susie's plane is leaving the _____ at 7 a.m. tomorrow morning.
   a bus station   c guest house
   b airport   d hotel

2 **A:** Felipe, do you want to do something together on Saturday?
   B: Yes, I really want to visit the new computer _____ . It sounds really good.
   a restaurant   c museum
   b theatre   d cinema

3 The _____ at the end of the road didn't have your medicine, so I went to the one on Hill Street.
   a bookshop   c pharmacy
   b bank   d college

4 Jerome broke his arm, so he went to _____ .
   a hospital   c supermarket
   b pharmacy   d library

5 My brother and I go swimming at the _____ near our house.
   a museum   c theatre
   b bookshop   d sports centre

6 **A:** Where can I get a gift for my friend?
   B: You can try the _____ in the city centre.
   a pharmacy   c college
   b library   d department store

7 **A:** Mum, I need some new shoes. Can I go and buy them this afternoon?
   B: OK. I'll go to the _____ to get some money.
   a bank   c hospital
   b pharmacy   d post office

8 I often study at the _____ . It's nice and quiet.
   a post office   c bookshop
   b department store d library

9 Mum and I had a delicious lunch at the Polish _____ on King Street.
   a restaurant   c station
   b theatre   d hotel

10 **A:** Do you often watch films at home?
   B: No, I don't. I usually go to the _____ with friends.
   a café   c cinema
   b theatre   d museum

Grammar

2 **Choose the correct answer.**

1 **A:** Do you like old buildings, Tamara?
   B: Not really. I like _____ building across the street. It's more modern.
   a those   c these
   b this   d that

2 Be quiet and listen to _____ song. Do you like it?
   a these   c this
   b those   d that

3 **A:** Excuse me, does _____ bus here go to the city centre?
   B: No, you need to take that bus over there.
   a that   c these
   b those   d this

4 **A:** This department store's got great swimming costumes.
   B: I prefer _____ at the small shop on Oak Street.
   a the ones   c one
   b ones   d the one

5 Kaleb is from _____ Israel.
   a a   c –
   b an   d the

6 Have you ever been on a boat trip on _____ river Thames?
   a an   c a
   b the   d –

7 How many people have walked on _____ moon?
   a –   c an
   b the   d a

8 **A:** There's a hotel near here with cheap rooms.
   B: Are you talking about _____ hotel on Jameson Street?
   a a   c –
   b an   d the

9 Is there _____ Italian restaurant in the city centre?
   a –   c an
   b a   d the

10 We went skiing in _____ Alps last year. It was really good fun!
   a an   c the
   b a   d –

Vocabulary

1 **Choose the correct answer.**

1 I enjoy _____ because I like using a camera.
   a painting   **c** photography
   b music   **d** camping

2 **A:** Do you want to play chess?
   B: Sure, I love _____!
   a drawing   **c** singing
   b board games   **d** dance

3 Do you do any sport? I love _____.
   a cycling   **c** singing
   b camping   **d** painting

4 **A:** What do you do in the evenings when
   you _____?
   B: We sit around the fire and tell stories.
   a paint   **c** dance
   b play music   **d** go camping

5 I love _____ because I really enjoy using colours.
   a dancing   **c** singing
   b cycling   **d** painting

6 She practises the _____ every afternoon.
   a violin   **c** concert
   b MP3 player   **d** radio

7 What do you do _____ your free time, Martha?
   a to   **c** in
   b at   **d** on

8 I like most types of music, but I'm not really _____
   opera.
   a on   **c** into
   b about   **d** for

9 I'm not crazy _____ chess.
   a in   **c** about
   b to   **d** with

10 I don't like _____ music because there are no
   electric guitars.
   a hip hop   **c** classical
   b disco   **d** pop

Grammar

2 **Choose the correct answer.**

1 When water becomes very cold, it _____ into ice.
   a turning   **c** turns
   b is turning   **d** turn

2 I'm sure that if you study, you _____ the exam.
   a passes   **c** pass
   b passed   **d** 'll pass

3 If we _____ at the concert early, we'll be near
   the stage.
   a arrived   **c** will arrive
   b arrives   **d** arrive

4 We _____ all the stars at night if we go to the
   countryside.
   a not see   **c** sees
   b saw   **d** can see

5 I miss _____ to the robotics club during the school
   holidays.
   a go   **c** to go
   b going   **d** to going

6 I will buy everyone's tickets _____ I get to the
   theatre.
   a where   **c** when
   b who   **d** how

7 **A:** What's wrong, Sam?
   B: I don't want _____ the guitar today. I feel
   really tired.
   a to practise   **c** practising
   b to practising   **d** practise

8 **A:** Does Eli still make jewellery?
   B: No, he stopped _____ it a long time ago.
   a to making   **c** make
   b to make   **d** making

9 Yusuf promised _____ my science book tomorrow.
   a return   **c** to return
   b to returning   **d** returning

10 **A:** Did you talk to Pedro yesterday?
   B: No, I forgot _____ him.
   a to call   **c** to calling
   b calling   **d** call

Vocabulary

1 **Choose the correct answer.**

1. A: Do you like _____ ?
   B: Yes, I love all team sports!
   a golf   c volleyball
   b swimming   d cycling

2. How often do you go _____ ?
   a baseball   c badminton
   b surfing   d rugby

3. Kaito's football _____ used to play in the national team.
   a winner   c coach
   b fan   d member

4. You use a _____ when you play cricket.
   a racket   c bat
   b bike   d club

5. Can you play _____ with just four players?
   a cycling   c basketball
   b skiing   d sailing

6. A: Does every animal have at least two _____ ?
   B: Yes, but some animals have got a lot more.
   a eyes   c necks
   b backs   d faces

7. My arm really hurts. I think I've _____ a bone.
   a felt   c cut
   b broken   d had

8. When we eat, food goes into our _____ .
   a nose   c hand
   b finger   d stomach

9. I practised baseball for three hours today. I _____ really tired!
   a feel   c hurt
   b have   d go to

10. Carole ate something bad. Now she _____ a stomach ache.
    a gets   c has
    b goes   d feels

Grammar

2 **Choose the correct answer.**

1. _____ I borrow your swimming goggles?
   a Could   c Should
   b Must   d Shouldn't

2. Dad, _____ take me to football practice at 4 p.m.?
   a can I   c you can
   b can you   d I can

3. You _____ ride your bike at night without lights. It isn't safe.
   a needn't   c mustn't
   b don't have to d must

4. Mr Horta, _____ ask a question about Exercise 2?
   a I may   c may I
   b I can   d may

5. A: What advice can you give me about snowboarding?
   B: It's fun, but it can be dangerous. You _____ take some lessons first.
   a may   c should
   b mustn't   d can

6. You _____ tell the coach if you're going to be late for basketball practice.
   a needn't   c mustn't
   b don't have to d must

7. You _____ bring golf clubs. I've got some extra ones you can use.
   a mustn't   c must
   b have to   d don't have to

8. You _____ follow the club rules.
   a have to   c don't have to
   b needn't   d mustn't

9. A: What food are we going to bring with us for the journey?
   B: I think we _____ take sandwiches – they don't take much space.
   a shouldn't   c may
   b should   d need

10. _____ help me train for a marathon?
    a Could   c Could you
    b You could   d Could I

Vocabulary

1 Choose the correct answer.

1 Did you see the _____ about your headaches?
   a pilot   c doctor
   b waiter   d farmer

2 I spoke to the _____ and I booked an appointment with Mrs Singh for Monday.
   a receptionist   c engineer
   b journalist   d shop assistant

3 My brother Hassan _____ as a waiter in a hotel.
   a wears   c works
   b gives   d earns

4 I have to give a(n) _____ to my class on beach clean-ups.
   a presentation   c uniform
   b occupation   d company

5 We learned about creating apps in my _____ class.
   a art   c IT
   b music   d biology

6 A: Do you know where the Caspian Sea is?
   B: No, I don't. I'm terrible at _____ .
   a physics   c chemistry
   b history   d geography

7 Do you want to work _____ a computer company?
   a on   c for
   b to   d as

8 I studied hard, so I hope I will _____ my exam.
   a pass   c follow
   b get   d do

9 Did you _____ a good mark in your history exam?
   a do   c get
   b pass   d study

10 A: What subjects do you like _____ ?
   B: Drama and art!
   a following   c studying
   b remembering   d answering

Grammar

2 Choose the correct answer.

1 Is that the man _____ lives across from you?
   a where   c who
   b –   d which

2 A: Is this the article _____ you wrote for your class?
   B: Yes, it is. Would you like to read it?
   a this   c –
   b what   d who

3 The police officer _____ helped us was very friendly.
   a which   c –
   b when   d that

4 The nurse _____ we spoke to gave us a lot of useful information.
   a –   c how
   b where   d why

5 She finished her homework too _____ , so she made a lot of mistakes.
   a quickly   c hard
   b well   d good

6 The biology exam _____ I took the other day was really difficult.
   a when   c –
   b what   d who

7 A: Noah is a talented singer.
   B: I agree. He sings _____ .
   a bright   c beautiful
   b beautifully   d brightly

8 They arrived _____ for supper, so their food was cold.
   a well   c late
   b fast   d hard

9 I asked the waiter _____ if we could have lunch outside.
   a hungry   c politely
   b polite   d hungrily

10 This is a dangerous road. Please drive _____ .
   a quickly   c politely
   b angrily   d carefully

Vocabulary

1 Choose the correct answer.

1 It's late. I'll call a _____.
    a coach   c tram
    b bus   d taxi

2 The _____ sailed across the ocean towards the port of Southampton.
    a plane   c bus
    b train   d ship

3 A: Let's ride your _____ to the party.
    B: We can't. Ali wants to come with us.
    a taxi   c tram
    b motorbike   d bus

4 Do you think there will be enough space in a small _____ for all your furniture?
    a helicopter   c coach
    b taxi   d lorry

5 A: What's the problem, Kareena?
    B: We haven't got much _____ left. We need to stop here to get some.
    a wheels   c tickets
    b transport   d petrol

6 If we don't hurry, we'll _____ our flight.
    a miss   c pass
    b delay   d lose

7 When André arrived at his stop, he quickly got _____ the train.
    a off   c on
    b back   d up

8 A: I'm afraid I can't take you to the library this morning.
    B: That's OK. I'll _____ the bus.
    a pick   c catch
    b drive   d go

9 Can you pick me _____ from school this afternoon?
    a at   c up
    b out   d off

10 I'm not sure how we can _____ to the main road from here. Do you know the way?
    a get off   c get back
    b pick up   d arrive

Grammar

2 Choose the correct answer.

1 Breakfast _____ between 7 a.m. and 10 a.m.
    a serves   c served
    b is served   d serve

2 The hotel rooms _____ every day after 11 a.m.
    a are cleaning   c are cleaned
    b is cleaned   d cleaned

3 We left on time, but our flight _____ by the bad weather.
    a wasn't delayed   c isn't delayed
    b was delayed   d is delayed

4 The best photos _____ on the website.
    a are often shown   c are shown often
    b is often shown   d is shown often

5 A: Where can I buy a map?
    B: They _____ maps in the shop across the road.
    a don't sell   c are sold
    b sell   d aren't sold

6 A: How old is this school building?
    B: It _____ in 1882.
    a were built   c built
    b is built   d was built

7 Why _____ yesterday?
    a was your flight cancelled
    b is your flight cancelled
    c your flight was cancelled
    d your flight is cancelled

8 A: Where were _____?
    B: In Colombia.
    a made these clothes   c these clothes make
    b these clothes   d these clothes made

9 A: What happened to your mobile phone?
    B: It _____ while I was on holiday.
    a were stolen   c is stolen
    b was stolen   d was stealing

10 A: How did you get home from the station yesterday?
    B: My uncle _____ me up because my parents were busy.
    a was picked   c picks
    b picked   d is picked

Vocabulary

1 Choose the correct answer.

1 **A:** Do I need to bring my umbrella?
   B: No, it's quite _____ at the moment.
   a sunny   c snowy
   b rainy   d stormy

2 The hills were covered in _____ and it was difficult
   to see them.
   a storms   c rain
   b wind   d fog

3 Paul wore a very heavy coat because it was _____
   outside.
   a cool   c warm
   b boiling   d freezing

4 _____ the weather like today?
   a What   c How's
   b Is it   d What's

5 **A:** Did you go sailing yesterday? It was nice and
   warm.
   B: No, we didn't. It was too _____ at the lake.
   a snowy   c windy
   b icy   d sunny

6 If the temperature gets _____, it will probably
   snow.
   a lower   c heavier
   b deeper   d stronger

7 **A:** Did you hear that _____ last night?
   B: Yes, I did. The storm came immediately after it.
   a hurricane   c thunder
   b drought   d wildfire

8 The plants are slowly dying because of the terrible
   _____ .
   a wildfire   c drought
   b hurricane   d thunder

9 **A:** Should we go for a bike ride? It's a bit windy.
   B: I think we'll be fine. There's just a _____ wind.
   a low   c weak
   b soft   d light

10 We should go inside soon. Some _____ clouds are
   coming.
   a dark   c strong
   b white   d light

Grammar

2 Choose the correct answer.

1 Brazil is much _____ than Iceland.
   a the warmest   c warm
   b warmest   d warmer

2 **A:** It's still very cloudy outside.
   B: I know. The weather looks _____ than it was
   this morning.
   a badly   c bad
   b worst   d worse

3 I think this autumn has been _____ wetter than
   last autumn.
   a more   c –
   b most   d very

4 **A:** It takes a long time to get to Ha-yoon's house.
   B: Oh, it isn't _____ far as you think.
   a the   c more
   b as   d most

5 **A:** Which subject do you prefer – science or
   history?
   B: I think history is _____ than science, so I prefer
   history.
   a as easy as   c easier
   b as easily as d more easily

6 We had the _____ storm of the year last night.
   A tree in our garden fell.
   a worst   c bad
   b badly   d worse

7 **A:** How was your hiking trip?
   B: It was the _____ holiday I've had for a long
   time!
   a better   c well
   b good   d best

8 It snowed a little in the morning and the afternoon,
   but it snowed the _____ during the night.
   a heavier   c most heavily
   b more heavily d heaviest

9 What's the _____ mountain in the world?
   a most highly   c higher
   b high   d highest

10 This is _____ programme I have ever seen.
   a the most boring   c most boring
   b more boring   d boring

Vocabulary

1 Choose the correct answer.

1 Let's go swimming in the _____ this weekend.
 a lake c desert
 b forest d mountain

2 Canada has got many beautiful _____ . If you love trees, it is a great place to visit.
 a rivers c forests
 b mountains d seas

3 I really enjoyed skiing in the Italian _____ last winter.
 a desert c forests
 b mountains d fields

4 There's a small _____ that goes through the centre of town.
 a lake c ocean
 b sea d river

5 Cyclists can also use the _____ along the river.
 a island c field
 b path d hill

6 We decided to start a vegetable garden, so we _____ some seeds.
 a grew c planted
 b made d put

7 I saw a group of _____ swimming in the Marmara Sea yesterday. It was amazing!
 a dolphins c snakes
 b bees d ducks

8 If you want birds in your garden, you should _____ a bird feeder.
 a grow c make
 b plant d save

9 What should we do to _____ after the planet?
 a look c spend
 b watch d see

10 _____ make honey. I love honey.
 a Dolphins c Butterflies
 b Bees d Sharks

Grammar

2 Choose the correct answer.

1 A: What did you get at the shop the other day?
 B: I got a _____ table.
 a round small plastic c small round plastic
 b plastic round small d round plastic small

2 I found a _____ bag on offer today for £5.
 a lovely green cotton c cotton lovely green
 b green cotton lovely d lovely cotton green

3 Can we recycle this _____ box?
 a metal long rectangular
 b long rectangular metal
 c rectangular metal long
 d metal rectangular long

4 They planted a _____ tree in their garden.
 a red short Japanese c Japanese red short
 b red Japanese short d short red Japanese

5 They're closing that _____ factory just outside of town.
 a grey scary c dangerous old
 b old scary d grey dirty

6 A: We saw lots of snakes at the zoo the other day.
 B: Oh, that sounds scary. I think snakes are _____ .
 a frightened c interesting
 b frightening d interested

7 I want to see the documentary about butterflies. It sounds _____ .
 a bored c interesting
 b boring d interested

8 I don't really like walking in the forest. I think it's _____ .
 a interesting c tired
 b interested d tiring

9 A: There's so much rubbish on the streets.
 B: I know. I'm _____ to see it. Why don't people use the bins?
 a amazed c interested
 b amazing d interesting

10 The city is going to close some streets to traffic, which is _____ news.
 a excited c tiring
 b exciting d tired

National Geographic Learning,
a Cengage Company

New Close-up A2 Workbook, 3rd Edition
Author: Phillip McElmuray

Publisher: Rachael Gibbon

Executive Editor: Siân Mavor

Senior Development Editor: Sarah Ratcliff

Director of Global Marketing: Ian Martin

Product Marketing Manager: Anders Bylund

Heads of Regional Marketing:

  Charlotte Ellis (Europe, Middle East and Africa)

  Irina Pereyra (Latin America)

Senior Content Project Manager: Nick Ventullo

Media Researcher: Jeffrey Millies

Art Director: Brenda Carmichael

Operations Support: Avi Mednick

Manufacturing Manager: Eyvett Davis

Manufacturing Buyer: Elaine Bevan

Composition: SPi Global

For permission to use material from this text or product,
submit all requests online at **cengage.com/permissions**
Further permissions questions can be emailed to
permissionrequest@cengage.com

Workbook ISBN: 978-0-357-43402-4

National Geographic Learning
Cheriton House, North Way,
Andover, Hampshire, SP10 5BE
United Kingdom

Locate your local office at **international.cengage.com/region**

Visit National Geographic Learning online at **ELTNGL.com**
Visit our corporate website at **www.cengage.com**

Printed in the United Kingdom by CPI Antony Rowe
Print Number: 02 Print Year: 2021

FSC
MIX
Paper from
responsible sources
FSC® C013604